A Claim in the Hills

JAMES WICKENDEN

A Claim
in the Hills

ILLUSTRATED BY RALPH THOMPSON

RINEHART & COMPANY, INC. New York

AUTHOR'S NOTE

Where the borders of Brazil, Venezuela and British Guiana meet, the frontier traditions of South America are carried on by the diamond prospector known as a "pork-knocker." Like the fur trapper of North America, he feels free and hopes to be wealthy. He has a peculiar nostalgia for pioneering. In these highlands of sandstone, ironstone and vine, pork-knockers do find grounds, but few stay to work the virgin lode conscientiously: they move on, satisfied at having seen unknown valleys and probed hidden creeks, dreaming of returning some day to dig them. Their pleasure is to have handled in quiet mornings the smooth mica, quartz and carbon from their pans that tell of a fortune around them in gold and diamonds.

The pork-knocker knows he can earn his keep by scraping his claims, and in a few days take out enough for a spree, send a year's keep to his wife, whether she is in Martinique, Georgetown or Boa Vista, then go back. His life is a potent mixture of lotus-eating, Spartan endurance and the thrill of discovery. Once he knows what lies beyond the savannah, the prospector is usually seduced: he forgets the crude intention of making a fortune and returning to a cramped civilisation, preferring to loaf in the grandiose diamond country.

Like all frontiersmen, the pork-knocker has to come to terms with the natives of the country—for him, the Amerindian tribes which have given us such words as hammock, barbecue and Caribbean. Many of these tribes are no longer strange, but some in the inland mountains, in whose foothills roam the pork-knockers, are little known even today. The English explorer, Colonel Fawcett, pointed out that exploration in South America has necessarily been along the rivers, where travel is easiest; the last fastness he said, would be in the inter-river mountains, and the tribes there the last to be studied. Since he vanished while searching for lost cities, there have been several large expeditions, notably in recent years by the French.

A few pork-knockers, bolder than the rest, have gone beyond their usual grounds and have explored haphazardly, sometimes for years, alone. Such men are unhandy with a pen, but one or two have the eye of the solitary resourceful traveller in sympathy with his landscape.

This work is entirely based on the experiences of one of these prospectors, a British West Indian and a personal friend of the author, who wishes to remain anonymous. The author has aimed to present a faithful portrayal of this man's life and of the Patamona with whom he lived. Only two changes to the facts have been made: the author has written in the first person, and he has linked isolated events to mirror more effectively life as it can be lived in the Patamona hills.

CONTENTS

A Claim in the Hills

CHAPTER ONE

With the Macoushi

THERE are probably no more than about two hundred prospectors, officials and traders, all told, in the many thousands of square miles of the Brazilian-Guiana border-country. In these lands seven is a crowd and fifteen miles a long way. Many of the prospectors come from around Boa Vista in Brazil and work in the foothills of the Pakaraiman ranges, although the Pakaraimas do not begin in Brazil, but northeast at Orinduik—a place without a street, a horse, or a mark on most maps of British Guiana. It is only a patch on the sandy savannah uplands by the banks of the Ireng River with

3

an irregular row of whitewashed, thatched or tin-roofed shanties, and some fishing nets drying over a pile of timber. In the store the straw-hatted prospectors get drunk on rum at a pound sterling a bottle. If a man has made a strike he orders several shelves of liquor and if he is overcharged it adds to the grand gesture of waste that he enjoys making among his drinking partners. They come with bare feet, many of them with a sweat band at their waists, Chinese, Portuguese, half-blood Indians, and a few Americans and West Indians.

From Orinduik the Indian territory of the Pakaraimas looks vast and strange. Great sandstone lumps stand above the jungle, weathered and riddled by sun and rain, the sand and gravel lying loose here and there in the savannahs; stunted hardwood "sandpaper" trees, which clap in the wind and make strangers turn round, dot the baldness of the flat-topped mountains. Higher, the ground is covered by a soft moss half an inch thick. It would make a comfortable place for a siesta were it not for the snakes.

Where the creeks open out and run down gentle slopes, the jungle begins suddenly like a thicker pelt, as if shaved neatly at the edges so that the trees should not show too much above the rim of the hills. Through the gloom of the jungle the howler monkeys scream and life quickens. It runs in a grand cycle, the goodness sucked from sodden leaves through different species of life into the sky two hundred feet above. The creatures live one above the other, keeping to their levels like flat dwellers in twelve-storied buildings of tangled wood. When they die they drop down with fluttering leaves and the crash of tall trees to the insect level and rot there to start the life-cycle once more. Instead of being nature's great muddle, as strangers have thought, the jungle is an intricate web of life, sustaining in it the prototypes of many creatures and trees on which civilisation depends.

The springs drain out of the mountains into the creeks and the broad rivers, in whose shadows the Indians in the red loin cloths which they call *saloes* come down to hunt in their

4

curee-ole canoes with six-foot bows. Macoushi, Arawak, Wai-Wai and Patamona, they are part of the jungle and know it as well as the freedom which they cherish above everything.

When I arrived at Orinduik I knew nothing of the jungle except what my father had told me, and I came alone with an Arawak Indian guide named Pablo, who was one of the Indians who had taken to town life and had the mixture of assurance and cunning that results from it. In my boxes I had brought the usual supplies: about £500 worth of cotton prints, beads, gunpowder, buckshot and guns, cased up tight to prevent probing with arrows.

We flew up in the old Dakota that makes the journey from the coast twice a month. As soon as we had bumped to a stop on the savannah airstrip we began to unload in front of a few tattered Indians. Pablo officiously set them to work and soon we had a camp on the side of the airstrip. When we had slung our hammocks and set a tarpaulin over the boxes I walked to the local store. On my return, Pablo said that he thought he would spend the next day finding carriers from the Macoushi tribe which lived nearby, to carry the stores into the hills.

In the morning he wanted something on account, and I gave him a new gun. I realised my error after three days had gone by without a sign of him. I was now on my own, unable to speak any local tongue and without help from the storekeeper, who foresaw no business with me with my mound of stores. My original plan had been carelessly framed: I had depended on Pablo who, in Georgetown, had spun a yarn about an American expedition he had led to riches in the mountains. He had gone, presumably back to his village, where no doubt he was the toast of the day with his new gun. I sat in the shade and opened a few tins to cook a meal hoping that, since Indians frequently came to Orinduik for trading, I might find another guide.

Next day three Indians stood around my camp; they showed interest and appeared to me to be genuine. The men wore loin-cloths, bead bands below their knees and on their

5

upper arms, and carried long bows, with the strings unstrung and the bow and arrows tied to be carried in one hand. The woman of the party wore a bead skirt. They began pointing at the stores, smiling encouragingly, and eventually I cracked open a case and handed them some rolls of cotton prints. They soon had the cloth unrolled and became excited, swinging their arms and pointing to the mountains and then to the sky. I imagined they meant I was to wait for the full moon which was in about three days' time. Sure enough on the fourth morning they returned with four more, including an old man.

His sunken eyes and long nose reminded me of a bird. He spoke a little English and was obviously accustomed to strangers. He paid little attention to what I said, merely nodding with a croak, "Aiye. Aiye." He explained that he was Garcia of the Macoushi tribe, and he would take me to Chinapouk, his village, about three days' march away. The supplies would be carried by the men in stages. We set off at once and reached Chinapouk in the three days. It was my first sight of a real Indian village: a large circular hut stood in a white sandy clearing by a river bank, surrounded by about thirty men, crones and children among the water gourds in the sand.

They began asking questions at once and Garcia answered. As soon as the tumult subsided he ordered the men to set up a camp for me about thirty yards away. I discovered from Garcia that the young woman had gone into the bush to hide. That night I sat with the men around the customary fire in the hut and answered them through Garcia. They wanted to know exactly why I was wandering in the hills. Cautiously I said I was taking pictures and collecting jaguar skins. They asked why, in that case, had I brought shovels. To bury the carcasses, I lied. They smiled and said nothing.

The women had crept back and the hut was full. There was no privacy: the married couples slept in hammocks by the side of each of the eight entrances, the girls slept between them to prevent visitations in the night, and the young men were on the other side of the hut. As they stared at me, now in a more friendly way, I noticed a rank smell, which later I

6

came to realise came from the Macoushi habit of eating fish in a half-cooked state, as well as worms and small insects.

Feeling that they were trying to be hospitable, I fetched three bottles of rum from my camp. At once they called it *cassili,* their cassava liquor. Garcia said I was a good man. This is particularly flattering praise from Indians, but, however, the attitude usually lasts only for a short time. As they became drowsy I slipped out and hung a tarpaulin over one side of my camp for privacy and went to sleep.

I did very little for the next three months but spend my time with the Macoushi, learning their ways and some of their language. I had plenty of stores and there seemed to be no hurry; moreover, I remembered my father's advice that to succeed in prospecting I must hasten slowly. Since the Indians were the key to the country, I let them set the pace. Gradually I took to the peaceful and simple existence. Time was unimportant, money unnecessary and the skills of the Indians fascinating. As soon as I had got over initial prejudices I realised that they were as finely adjusted to their environment as a scholar in his study or a farmer in his fields; added to which their life was complete and self-contained, without demands from an outer world, fears of authority or envy of neighbours. Even Garcia's frontier cunning dropped away from him as he became the natural patriarch of his little community.

One evening Garcia told me that tomorrow would be a day for hunting. It was early next morning when I heard them moving about, the mist from the hills still rising. It was the quiet hour before dawn. I could hear the creak of straps as the women put on their *warishis,* which are baskets used for carrying, to go to the patches of burnt jungle where they grew the bitter cassava. Cassava contains prussic acid and is poisonous if boiled as a vegetable, but it is gathered all over South America to make bread. First the cassava is pulverised on wooden graters called *aki-yai*—"cassava-wood"—made from curved planks embedded with flints. After grating, the cassava paste is put into a *mata-pee,* a cylindrical

7

basket closed at one end, which is woven from the eetae palm fibre and hung from a beam outside the house. Through its base is thrust a pole and on either side the children sit to draw down and contract the basket. The paste is squeezed and the cassava liquor drips out into gourds. This is used on the coast to starch clothes, but the Indians make from it their favorite cassili liquor. The cassava paste is spread to dry in large palm leaves in the sun, and then baked in clay pans to form cakes about an inch thick and two feet in diameter. These methods are common all over the Indian territory in South America.

The women set to work baking and making liquor, paying little attention to the hunting party, but apparently in no doubt that the men would return with meat. The men now gathered with their bows and muzzle-loaders: *aragebuzas* they called them, a corruption from the Spanish *arquebuz*. They also carried spears and short knives. After they had strung their bows, I joined them with some powder and shot which I handed to those with guns. The hunting party stripped to their red *saloes* and we went down the short slope to the river to load the *curee-ole* canoes. No one saw us off, and we paddled away in the still dawn, the dripping paddles sounding alone in the silence.

The river was a tributary of the Ireng, but even at this distance from the sea, about two hundred miles, it was a large and powerful stream, in places half a mile wide but narrowing in gorges to fifty feet, and swift-flowing. We moved upriver, ten men in two canoes, and at a mile from the camp the hunt began. The tactics were for the canoes to divide, one to each side of the river, so that there was a party for each bank. All the men disembarked except the steersmen. While the parties fanned out in a semicircle through the jungle of their respective banks, the steersmen paddled a further half-mile upstream. Then they allowed their canoes to drift slowly down while they fished and passed the time until the hunters in the jungle had picked up the trails. The timing was exact, so that as the hunting parties moved downstream

8

the canoes would be parallel with them, and any game startled towards the river bank would be covered by the steersmen. The steersmen also acted as links between the two parties across the river, who talked to each other by whistles. This whistling is not merely confined to isolated signals, but is a phonetic copy of the spoken word, so that a complete conversation can be carried on as if the whistlers faced each other. But the notes are whistled in such a way that animals will imagine them to be bird-calls.

Owing to lack of skill, I was not allowed to go with the hunting party and stayed in one of the *curee-oles*. Garcia always kept close to me and stayed as steersman. By the time we reached the starting point the sun was up and the harsh-voiced parakeets were swarming to their feeding grounds in flocks of sixty to a hundred. The men got out silently and vanished in a few seconds into the high, thick jungle, moving barefooted at great speed, picking their way through the tangled undergrowth. Garcia and I paddled on upstream for the extra half-mile.

I offered Garcia a cigarette. "Me got smoke," he said, and I noticed that he was pushing a ball of something from one side of his mouth to the other. He produced what looked like a small lump of green fungus which he put to his teeth and drew in the aroma two or three times. "What is it, Garcia?" I asked. The old man paddled on, his eyes darting about, missing nothing, and began smiling with his whole face, crinkling round the eyes, as if laughing silently. Indians rarely laugh out loud. He pointed to the mountain: "Big water-fall." He rubbed the side of the canoe in a scraping action. "Big stone," he said. I realised that it must be some kind of moss. He produced a tiny gourd containing lumps of this *coue-ga* moss and offered me a bit. I tried it. It was very salty and I chewed until it formed a mass: only then did it begin to emit a very powerful aroma that made me feel dizzy, like the effect of chloroform. I slung it over the side. Garcia began to laugh properly this time, and shouted across the river about the *turung mati*, the stranger, and his taste of the *coue-ga*.

9

Garcia changed the subject by pointing out the fruits growing along the bank. There were waiti beans and sac, a red fruit shaped like a carrot, which were both edible; and many others not edible at that season. We reached the half-mile limit and Garcia signalled to the other canoe to stop paddling. The canoes turned round and we began drifting downstream. We had no time for conversation now. A sharp continuous whistling started up from our party. "What's happening, Garcia?" I asked. He held up his hand for silence and looked at the sky listening intently. He turned to the other canoe and shouted "*Mypuri, mypuri!*" The two steersmen began paddling their canoes furiously downstream.

As we drew nearer to the calls Garcia stood up in his canoe and gave a loud yell which echoed between the jungle walls, to say he was in position. A high, drawn-out call came back and we knew the hunters were pressing the chase. Excitedly I asked what was happening. "Wild cow," he said. It was a tapir heading for the river bank. One party of the hunters was nearby and I could hear branches breaking as they trampled about, now careless of being noisy. Suddenly the tapir broke out on to the river bank with three arrows sticking out of its rump, a grey seven-hundred-pound bunch of agitated muscle, thick-skinned with the face of an ass. It threw itself into the river with a splash and submerged for twenty yards. The other canoe had collected four of its party and both canoes raced downstream after him. The men fitted collapsible arrows to their bows: with these arrows the haft is flung clear on impact leaving the head buried, to which is attached a long thin cord fastened to the hunter's wrist. The tapir came up again, blowing spray from its nostrils and seeking air. The men were standing in the canoes keeping perfect balance and they all fired at once. The lines snaked out and three arrows thudded into their marks, under the jaw and behind the shoulder.

The big bull dived again and the hunters let out more line. The canoes followed up on the beads of bubbles streaming from him swimming below. He made his final ascent and swam on the surface downstream; beginning to weaken, he pointed his snout to the far bank. The other canoe headed him off to keep him in the centre, all the men silent and watchful. Finally when he swam slowly Garcia signalled to drive him to the bank. He pointed to my gun and nodded and put his hand on his ear. I was to kill him as he reached the bank by a shot in the ear.

As the tapir approached the bank the canoes drew ahead to prevent him dashing off into the jungle with the cords, which were still tied to the hunters' wrists, for he could easily have dragged the boatload after him. As he floundered and reared through the soft mud towards the bank, I fired three shots quickfire from my repeater, blowing away most of his jaw. This finished him and he lay still in the mud. One of the men cut a long vine, while others cut a branch which was lashed between the canoes, so holding them apart. They dragged the tapir into the water and fastened his legs to the branch with the vine, leaving his body in the water where its weight was neutralised. So we drifted downstream to the village. Everyone was talking excitedly at the swift kill. As we drew near to home the long high yell went out to announce success.

Garcia told me to follow the men and we climbed the steep clay bank in which footholds had been cut by hardwood shovels. Chinak ropes led down from the village. These ropes are made by stripping the chinak creeper from the mora tree and beating it until soft. Although they are not woven, chinaks will take a steady strain of about half a ton. We left the tapir lying below in the mud. As the single file of our party emerged from the gloom into the village clearing, the old women bustled about calling "tata niko, tata niko—bring all the knives!" The men paid no attention, as their duty was done, and we went into the big house. At the doorways the young women served out bowls of cassili liquor.

"I won't drink cassili," I told Garcia. "I have my own rum."

"You drink cassili," he replied. "Buck man vexed you no drink." I saw that it was useless to object. The cassili was fresh and therefore slightly bitter, and it gave my mouth the dry, astringent taste of strong stewed tea. I sipped slowly and the others had finished many bowls by the time I had drunk my first. As we drank, the women's voices came up from the river where they were quartering the meat. Occasionally there was a short groan, a curious Indian sound for disappointment, usually followed by expressive glances. I asked Garcia why they groaned. "Girls keep plenty noise—feel happy. Other noise when they find buckshot in meat." He explained that any meat with buckshot in it would be cut out and thrown away. This is always done wherever an animal is scarred or in any way disfigured.

I was feeling slightly sick from the cassili when I came out of the hut and the sight of the meat was not appetising. The women had barbecued it in large pieces on sticks which were supported on uprights over a fireplace. A huge clay pot was boiling at the side, into which they were throwing the entrails after washing them. The skin of the animal was slung under the barbecue with the hair downwards, so that it seemed that no part of the animal would be wasted. The men were still drinking but there was no sign of drunkenness, although they were preparing for a feast that would go on for three days continuously. As soon as the meat was cooked through, and the fat dripped sizzling into the fire, they squatted in a circle, and cut shreds off with their knives to eat. They did not hurry and, after filling their bellies, they would talk endlessly with each other for diversion and then start again. All through the night the eating and resting continued, while the fat dripped and sent the flames leaping into the darkness. So the tapir cooked in the heat of his own fat and his innards bubbled in the cauldron, making a vast store of soup heavily spiced with wiri-wiri pepper, which was left outside the house for the next three weeks, gradually being consumed by any passer-by, who would dip a piece of cassava bread into the brew for refreshment. The skin, now a shrivelled length of crackling, was also kept to the last, and any hunter going off on the trail would cut a slice and chew the tough hide on his march. That night I left them and went back to my camp to cook a piece of the tapir out of a selection of steaks they had offered me.

When the cold hours came after midnight the men finally gave up and slept, but as soon as the sun rose the whole village began once more to feast and drink, although by this time the meat was cold. I would have felt isolated from them if Garcia had not often come across to talk. Most of the time we would teach each other our languages, particularly the words for natural objects such as moon, trees, water, birds, and so on, but sometimes all the men came to talk of bigger things. Although Garcia was a persuasive and accepted teacher of his hamlet, I soon discovered that even he could not pass on to them the ideas of the outside world which we take for granted; the oceans, the continents, and their cities. About them they would always be interested, and one morning they sat round my hammock and we talked about planes. They were near enough to the frontier occasionally to see the plane coming over to land at Orinduik, and some of course had seen it on the ground. They sat silent and staring steadily at me as I told them that bigger planes went across seas to distant lands and cities.

One of the older men began asking Garcia a question. Another broke in and seemed to be reframing the question. Then another spoke. They nodded, in their manner, slowly.

"How the big bird go?" was the considered query of this brains trust.

I pointed to one of their lamps, a clay globe with a hole in the top into which is fed the flaky iowa wax from a jungle resin, which burns away without melting.

"When that wax is finished," I said, "the lamp goes out. Big bird also carries a kind of wax but it is like water. This burns inside and makes it go. When the water wax is finished the big bird cannot fly and rests on the ground."

Silence and stares, then the questions between them, until one spokesman had satisfactorily reframed their views.

13

"Fire inside big bird no good," they said.

"The big bird's fire does not send out flame. It burns very quickly and gives out heat like the sun and it is trapped to make it work," I replied.

After a brief discussion they said I was lying. Quickly I reflected on my words and realised that I had made a mistake in choosing one of their own things, the lamp, as an illustration.

"You know the noise the big bird makes," I said. They said they knew its noise. "It is the same noise as thunder makes," I continued. They agreed. I paused and pointed at the men around me.

"Garcia," I said, "what man here can say how the thunder works even after he has heard it many times?"

"No man," they said. This curious retort satisfied them and that was the end of the discussion on planes.

It was the dry season, about mid-August, and the river was low. The hunters of other tribes were out beyond their normal boundaries in search of game and large fish, which at this time are only found below the headwaters. Garcia's villagers sensed their presence, although I heard no gunshots or other sounds and saw no sign of them. I was eager to see them, as I was beginning to feel the restriction of the Macoushi settlement at Chinapouk and had got no further with my original plans. My stores of flour were becoming caked and the salt and sugar were already moist and soggy; the pickled meat was dried up and my tinned stocks were low. It was time, I decided, to make a move and the hunting fever in the air made an opportunity seem ripe.

One morning I noticed that Garcia had little time to speak to me. He kept going out on short walks, to the river and into the bush, and he sent two or three *curee-oles* up-river manned by boys as scouts. It was quiet until late morning, when I heard the faint pounding of paddles on the sides of *curee-oles*. This is always the first hint of an Indian on the rivers: at every stroke the paddle strikes the side of his craft and the sound carries for at least a mile on still nights and

14

in the day for about half that distance. The sound of many paddles signified a large party. Garcia came over to me where I sat on a massive stone trying to estimate the sounds. He was quite excited, speaking to me but looking towards the river with a frown. He pointed to the river.

"*Kapung* come. *Kapung* come. Not good people." I understood that men of another tribe were approaching. Before I could reply he went on, "*Kapung* eat your food quick time—one moon two moon. Garcia people good people. His people take long time to eat your food." I considered his quaint plea but decided that I would go if there was a chance. But this incident showed me for the first time that when Indians have accepted a person they do not want to let him go. It seemed a good opportunity to press my plans on Garcia and make him lead me to the diamond deposits of which he must know. In the same instant I wondered how long his co-operation would last.

"You show me good places diamonds?" I asked.

"Got good place. Got good place. Plenty, plenty," he replied. He would have promised me the moon. I could already see the *curee-oles* coming down the river. The water was still and sparkling; the noon sun shone on the small fish beneath. The mist still clung to the bends and inlets beneath dripping trees and the boats cut cleanly, sending strong wavelets to the bank. In the bow an Indian bent at each stroke and the others followed in their turn so that the paddles entered the water in succession like the rhythm of a centipede's legs. The steersman was chanting "*Naiee-le-Lai, Lai, Naiee-le-Lai,*" in a high musical tone. It means literally "where paddle" and conveyed: "Where the paddles are taking us—there we follow." The bow paddler answered these words with: "*Waki-bey-mang; Waki-bey-mang.*" It meant: "Very good man," and its message was: "The way is good." They seemed a virile crew.

Garcia followed my gaze and called me off the rock. "Come. Come me camp. Indian come." I was surprised. "No, I wait boat come landing. If you don't call them they won't come," I said. But I followed him to the camp. No one was stirring to give a welcome. Some lay in their hammocks; women were weaving fish lines and the babies sat, as usual, bawling in the cold, damp sand. One man lay under the barbecue playing with the dying embers with a bamboo splinter. It all seemed strange. Women never weave lines unless a fishing party is on the point of going out; the men never sit about with nothing to do: they would normally be at the fields, making new bows or cleaning their guns, since it was the hunting season. Clearly the Macoushi were putting on a show of domestic indifference. The noise of paddling had stopped, and I heard a shout from the river. "What do they say, Garcia?" I asked. "Don't know," he replied. I knew he was lying. I ran out of the camp and down the steep clay slope. The boat drifted with its crew of eight men and boys. They were naked except for *saloes* but all had guns, bows and spears, and the boat was stacked with sheaves of arrows and spare arms. They were murmuring as if in doubt about Garcia's village.

When they saw me one called out, much to my surprise, in English.

"Who you? Who you?"

"Come," I said. They all smiled and paddled to the bank. A few jumped out and held the boat steady. They offered their hands and we shook hands in greeting, also a surprising gesture. One called out, "You prospector?"

"Yes, but I punished plenty here." It seemed that with them there was no difficulty in speaking plainly.

One laughed. He could see the tarpaulin over my stores on the hill. "Plenty ration, How you punish with plenty ration?"

"No good creeks," I said, meaning it was too mountainous in the district for easy prospecting.

During this introduction, Garcia and his people had come up silently behind me and were lined up at the top of the slope gazing in silence. I asked the boat's crew to come up to my camp but they declined, saying that Garcia's lot looked

16

put out. So I sat down and began trying to arrive at some arrangement with them, asking first how far they were going and where their village was. I found out that they were of the Patamona tribe. The Patamonas are known at Orinduik as being more numerous than the Macoushi but more scattered; they also have the reputation of being willing but capable of subtle revenge should an agreement be broken. A Patamona may work hard every day of a year for the promise of a gun: should the gun not be forthcoming he will scheme for weeks to even the score.

I bargained with them, saying that I did not want their help but was willing to employ them in exchange for a definite amount of stores. They said that as they were on their hunt they would require compensation for leaving it. I agreed to this and it was settled that they would take me about eighty miles farther into the interior to their village, which lay about seven days' march overland from the river.

Dusk was falling and the cold mist was rising again by the time we got down to details. They were to go back in their *curee-ole* up-river to make a clearing where my supplies would be stacked, after which they would be carried overland. The *curee-ole* was to return to carry the supplies and myself. So after shaking hands they all left.

On return to the village Garcia came hurrying up to ask if the *kapungs* had gone away for good. "No," I said, "I am leaving with them tomorrow."

"Soon morning—breakfastsi *atai*—you go?"

He wanted to know the exact hour of my departure, either at first light or at midday. I parried by saying I would go soon in the morning, although in fact my rendezvous with the Patamonas was that night. I pulled down my tarpaulins and checked my supplies. None of the Macoushi lent a hand. I waited and heard no sound from the village. Apprehensively I counted the minutes until the return of the Patamonas. If they let me down I knew that I would be in the hands of the Macoushi, as it was impossible for me to move without some assistance. Then at about eight in the evening, although it was a dark moonless night, I heard the paddles once more striking a fast beat down-

17

stream, and soon three Patamonas came up with baskets strapped at their backs. Garcia had come over and stood in silence as they took the first load, looking at each case as it went. It took over an hour to load the boat. I left 300 pounds of flour, fifty pounds of salt and a tin of sugar, telling Garcia to keep an eye on them until I returned in the morning. He said nothing and shook his head: he was not sure but obviously suspected that this was some kind of parting gift. I went into the camp, by this time knowing how to say goodbye in their tongue. I stood in the centre of the house where they all lay swinging in their hammocks round the fire. No one moved as I entered: they had already begun to ostracise me. I told them that I was leaving when the sun had come up. No one answered. So I started to walk out of the house. Two little boys, who had become quite attached to me, ran from their tiny hammocks and clung round my ankles. They bent their heads murmuring a request for my knife. It was clear that they had not been sent and wanted something to remember me by. I took the knife from my belt and gave one the knife and the other the sheath. They did not thank me—Indians never do—and went back to sit by the fire and gaze at their gifts.

Garcia was standing at the door, so I told him that I would sleep at the landing and return in the morning. He said that he would come with me and return in the morning to help with the goods. "No," I said, "you keep an eye on what I have left." He agreed, and I walked a few steps and looked back at Garcia, standing apparently simple and bewildered.

CHAPTER TWO

To the Patamona

THE Patamona are shorter and stockier than the Macoushi and the designs of their bead garments, especially of the women's aprons, are more elaborate. Unlike the Macoushi, they have little inclination to intermarry with other tribes or even with other families. Consequently intermarriage between close blood relatives is common, and this may perhaps account for their very short life-span: it is common for a man to die between thirty and forty, although there are some old men. However, to compensate for their weakness of blood, the Patamona go on long expeditions to hunt and fish for good food, which the Macoushi do not, being content with whatever is near at hand.

The primary object of the Patamona, as of all Indians, is to survive. This fact permeates everything they do and believe, although they would be unable to say so. With these Indians all appears to the outsider as simple on the surface and reveals inner depths only after some acquaintance.

This may be so because it is at the point where the conscious everyday mind touches the lower depths of insight and intuition that the Indian develops himself. Civilised man nurtured in a scientific age usually strives to be "objective" and to calculate: his faith is in the rational faculties of the mind. With the Indian it is not so. He is bad at calculation—few Amerindian tribes have words for numbers higher than ten—but from childhood he becomes adept at non-vocal insight. His perceptions are quickened. He thinks a great deal and is intensely alive to events and his surroundings, but not with the intention of formulating "ideas." Survival is his main aim, but his sensitivity is acute to subtle pleasures and meanings. An Indian lazing in a hammock is as busy in his mind as a book lover relishing and criticising the style and content of what he reads, but he would convey his thoughts by currents of feeling, a slight expression or a sigh. In short, he does not cultivate his mind to change the world but to suit it and extract his needs expertly.

In this attitude lies his strength and his weakness. I was to see much evidence of both in the next five years, but for the present I saw only the amazing ability of the Indian to live and move with safety and speed in a hostile world as we went on our seven-day trip into the mountains, and in it there was an aesthetic pleasure such as one finds in the skill of any craftsman the world over.

When I had settled myself in the loaded Patamona *cureeole*, the crew paddled up to the clearing in two hours. They told me to sit still as the boat was loaded to the gunwales. They were able to bend and thrust at the paddles without disturbing the balance of the boat. In a loaded boat the steersman does all the work and he does not speak at his task, for the boat must be moving all the time to prevent jerking and to keep dead straight into the river's stream. Even at bends the steersman keeps the boat in midstream and does not make use of slack water, since in coming out of slack water into the heavy stream the danger of capsizing is too great to be risked. This water held no threat of man-eating piranha fish and alligators, but in the mountain streams the water kamodie and the water labaria abound. The labaria is venomous, and the kamodie is a type of python about fifteen feet long, which kills by wrapping itself round its victim and crushing it to death.

Then darkness came and I wondered how the steersman was still able to keep dead in the centre of the stream. I glanced behind and saw that he was not looking at the water any more but up at the night sky. There the blackness of the trees on either side showed a clear channel between them as if the river had been projected above, and he steered by that, keeping in the centre. Without a word he pointed at the side, apparently at the landing. The paddlers worked on and we pushed farther upstream until he steered the boat as it went astern into the bank, where we secured and disembarked. Ten yards in from the bank was a hidden clearing with a blazing fire, invisible from the river.

I suggested that the stores be left in the boat till morning, but the steersman replied that it was better to unload now in case the water dropped in the night and stranded the boat out on the mud. They told me to sling my hammock and they would attend to the rest. I fixed it up between two trees and went to sleep almost at once while the crew worked between the boat and the clearing.

At dawn I was aroused by one of them. The stores were all there, but I discovered that three Patamonas had already left with three hundred pounds—a remarkable load of a hundred pounds for each of the little men, one of whom was only fifteen years old. They can manage these weights because of the way in which the straps are fixed to the *warishi* basket: two shoulder straps at the top and bottom of the oblong basket with no back into which the load is placed and strapped, and a head-band from the top. The Indian stoops to take the load so that his head is thrust forward into its strongest posture. With his chin tucked in he rises and walks on, not once raising his eyes for perhaps eight hours.

The *warishi* is formed from a main frame of tibisiri vine, a stiff kind of cane, light but springy. The walls are of woven tibisiri bark, and the largest *warishis* are designed for a top weight of about one hundred and twenty pounds. The tibisiri vine is also used for fishing baskets and *mata-pee*, the cassava strainers I first saw with the Macoushi. This strong vine grows as a parasite on large trees in all types of country and is chiefly recognised by its leaf which is short, thin and isolated from its neighbours along the vine. This lack of clustering leaves means few knobbly joints and may account for its strength.

All the *warishis* were loaded and also my rucksack of thirty-five pounds, which was heavy enough for me, although I was fit from the life I had spent. I was to go straight on for the eighty miles with one man while the rest walked back and forth in stages, one man being left behind to guard the *warishis* and the rest of the stores. Labba was appointed my guide. I knew this was the name they give to the tapir, one of the best eating animals of the jungle, which at a distance looks like an overgrown rat but has cleaner habits. Labba was unlike his namesake: in fact he was a handsome young buck of about seventeen, although his stomach was paunchy from eating the dried cassava powder which is called farine. Cassava powder is a perfect iron ration for long trips as it is light and yet filling, and keeps one going without hunger. But it builds up a thirst, and as it doubles its own weight in water, after a meal it swells in the stomach: the more one drinks the more it seems to swell. A habitual diet of this, which the Indians regard as a delicacy, gives many of them a paunch early in life.

Before we left I went down to the river, but the boat was gone. Labba said it was there but sunk to the river bottom and secured by two chinak ropes from bow to stern to overhanging trees. In this way the wood of the boat would remain in good condition indefinitely, away from the sun and mist.

After the first few miles of the trail the high razor grass was tiring: one has to stamp directly on it at each step as it is sharp enough to lash through drill cloth. But when the trees took over, the sandy trail we had passed became stony and matted with dead leaves and we rose on a gentle slope into thick jungle. The green light was restful and there were no mosquitoes as we came into the mountain country. On the first day's march we approached the lower spurs of the Paka-raima range. Most of the heights we were to march through were around the 3,000-foot mark. We walked until six in the evening when I estimated that we had covered about eleven miles, accomplished with a rest every three hours. We ate as we marched from handfuls of farine.

We did not notice the sunset in the jungle although dark-ness had crept on, and at six it was quite dark and we made camp. The Patamonas had the same inflammable iowa wax as the Macoushi but carried it in leaves instead of bottles. A buck produced a clay-coloured flint which he struck with the back of a knife to light a small bundle of dried leaves, and with this tinder lit the lumps of iowa and also our campfire. The hammocks were slung between the trees and I made coffee in my billy can. So the camp was made, and all of us flopped into our hammocks and went straight to sleep. I had blankets for the colder night on the hillside, but the bucks relied on the fire: they kept bundles of sticks under their hammocks which they slung on the blaze with-out rising. Anyone who turned over half asleep and saw the fire burning low slung his stick; in this way they fed the fire all through the night. Through the darkness the hollow boom of frogs, some far, some near, marked the long hours. At dawn they stopped and for the first time I heard the roar of the howler monkeys. Labba said it was a sure sign of the start of the rains, although I could see no rain clouds.

When the *warishis* were strapped on they were covered with huge wild banana tree leaves—in its wild state the banana bears little fruit but many of these useful umbrella leaves. We took to the trail again and there was no change in temperature or any sign of coming rain. After four hours' walk a stiff breeze blew along the trail and the booming of rain came from the surrounding mountains, but another hour passed before the rain reached us. At first the trees held it off, then it poured through almost solidly. We dropped our pace but pushed on. The rain did not seem to affect the Indians' naked bodies, though I shivered in my soggy clothes, envying the Patamonan toughness.

The rain came down for nine hours and then ceased abruptly, as if a vast tank had finally emptied. It was already dark and we made camp much later that day, so that we could reach open country and escape the dripping jungle. We cut poles and fitted up tripods for the hammocks: one main tripod in the centre held up one end of all the hammocks and smaller ones held up the outer ends. I said to Labba, "Too much weight on big poles."

"It's good," said Labba. "When one man get up from hammock the sticks spring and others know." It was, I realised, an automatic warning system in case of alarm from wild animals or sickness.

Next morning, from this camp Labba and I went on alone, leaving the porters to take the easier trail. He led me straight into the jungle and, for a time, there seemed to be no means of keeping direction. But every half-hour or so he looked up through the trees and took his bearings from the sun. Here and there we came across thin bamboos blazed by a passing hunter's knife. Upward slashes told of water on the downward slope, and downward cuts showed trails upwards through the hills. By these signs and the sun, Labba was as sure of his position as if he had been walking the streets of a town.

We came to some lana trees, which bear a sweet fruit in a thick shell, beneath which a nigger-coop bird was feeding, standing in a slanting ray of sun. It was about three feet high, jet black, with long legs and a long neck. It jerked up and watched us. We walked on silently over the matted leaves and it let us approach within four yards before setting off on its spindly legs. The nigger-coop is rare in these jungles but I had seen it fre-

24

quently around Garcia's village. We saw powice birds also which the Indians hunt for their meat. The powice looks like a large twenty-pound turkey with a black silky plumage and yellow beak, the hen having distinctive white spots. Labba pointed to one feeding on the ground. "Powice eat anything like diamond," he said.

It seems that they like anything which shines. This interested me, for if the powice had been feeding along creeks it might easily have picked up precious stones. There might even be some in its stomach I thought, so I asked Labba to shoot it.

He was carrying the usual Indian six-foot big game bow, which has arrows, between four and seven feet long, tipped with iron, bullet-wood tree or the flat bones of animals. Labba carried his bow unstrung in his hand with the arrows tied to it by the string. He undid the string, put the base end of the bow between his big toe and the next one, and with one movement swung out his knee against the bow, flexed in the upper end with one hand and slipped the string on with the other. It was done in an instant, more quickly than loading the magazine of a rifle. He crouched down, bringing the bow across his body to make a horizontal shot, used for small game so that the hunter can crouch: the vertical shot is for big game and long ranges. He crept a few paces, watching every movement of the bird about thirty feet away. The powice sensed something, but it had not seen us. It began walking in a circle darting glances about, to decide which way to make its run. Before it completed the first circle I saw the bow bend to full stretch in a smooth plucking action so that Labba fired just before reaching the limit of his pull. The arrow sped with a whirr along his aim, which he had taken through a funnel of tangled branches no bigger in places than a saucer. A shot gun would have lost most of its pellets in the branches before reaching the target, and I was impressed, especially when I found that he had hit the bird low in the neck, breaking it. This is the only fatal arrow shot for a powice. An arrow through any part of the body will not prevent them running into rocks or underbrush where they become inaccessible.

25

Labba confidently dropped his bow the instant he fired and wormed his way through the undergrowth still in a crouch, moving quickly near the ground where the going was easier. When we reached the powice it was jumping about. Labba waited. When it had finally settled he broke off the head of the arrow, withdrew the haft and flung it away. He turned to me as I plunged through the branches to him, calling me softly and personally for the first time.

"*Yapung*—friend, come. Come." When I reached him he pointed to the bird. "You take powice." I plucked the feathers off at once, before the bird was cold, so that they came off easily. Then I took Labba's knife and slit the breast to reach the guts. The powice has the same organs as a duck, that is, no crop but a proper stomach lying directly beneath the breast. I cut deeper and extracted a small pile of octahedral quartz crystals and shards of mica which were mixed in the mass of undigested seeds and other food. But no diamonds. On thinking it over, I felt that I had not been over-optimistic in hoping for them: where diamond-bearing gravel runs to the surface, as it often does, the powice might easily pick up one or two. Some prospectors tame powice as pets, but the Indians never do, for they are too destructive in a village, especially where beads are vital clothing.

Labba cleaned the powice, stuffed the legs in the incision, tied down the wings and let a strand of chinak through the nostrils in its beak. Slinging our twenty-pound bird ration on his back, he and I set off once more. For the next three days I plodded after his light steps through jungle and occasional patches of savannah, each night following the same camp routine. As there were only two of us, it was impossible to keep a fire going at night by throwing branches, so Labba usually found a large log and put one end under his hammock. Every now and then he leant over and shoved it into the blaze.

On the march we came across several deserted Indian hunting camps. First a small clearing is made around a small straight-growing tree. About three palm leaves eight feet long are cut and strapped at an angle from the tree making a tent

26

open at one end, where the camp fire is built. There the hunters crouch for the night, dozing on their haunches. They carry hammocks, which weigh three or four pounds, only when the family goes hunting with them.

It seemed as though we had walked for weeks when, on the last day, we rejoined the main trail, which ran along the bank of a stony watercourse in open savannah, and passed two patches of cultivated land totalling about five acres, mostly growing bitter cassava and banana trees, the latter planted in gullies to catch the rain water. They were also growing pepper and corn in small lots. As we reached the top of the hill the small houses came in view, three or four, not circular like the Macoushi huts, but square and thatched, with two doors only. No one vanished with the customary Macoushi shyness as I appeared. My mind, dazed from endless walking, cleared as the villagers came crowding round with smiles. They looked me up and down from top to toe, noting the smallest detail. I counted about twenty of them, making a small village by other standards, but twenty is many people in the jungle.

Labba was chattering away at a great rate, explaining that I was a prospector and that the others were following with my goods. The women asked most of the questions.

"What has he got?"

"Where did you meet him?"

"Is he alone on the trail?"

There was much shaking of heads and more smiles as Labba answered. Labba's father, to whom I had been introduced, was looking at my watch. He lifted my hand.

"Me know. Compass," he said. "No," I began. "Yes—compass," repeated the old man. He was quite sure of his facts. The children crowded round, not listening, their eyes big with uninhibited interest. Labba's father was the oldest Indian I had ever seen. His skin was leathery and crinkled and he walked slowly, although his back was as straight as a young buck's. I estimated his age to be about fifty-six. His left ear was punched and he wore in it a ring of brightly coloured beads; around his neck was a necklace of teeth from tigers, pig, deer, the wild

27

cow, and even snakes, all of which came from animals he had shot in his youth. There were gaps in the strings, presumably for more trophies. This collecting of teeth from their game is a hobby among Indians.

The women looked healthy and strong, and they were a more lively lot than the Macoushi. The young ones wore their hair down to their waists and the older ones plaited it and made a bun on the top of their heads. The bead bands below their knees and at their ankles were of bold and attractive design, mostly red, and suspended from strings around their necks were cotton tassels dyed with local plants and bark.

I was exhilarated. This was the heart of the mountain Indian country. The view stretched away to hazy blue ranges fifteen or more miles distant, and directly below the village the slope of sandstone boulders, in the cracks of which grew delicate ferns, descended gently to the fields and the creek. The village stood on the hill crest in a cool fresh breeze. No tall trees stood near to break the weather. The huge boulders, the silence and the clean feeling of the mountains made me think of a temple open to the sky.

I noticed a special house apart from the others. It had no walls and in front of it was a large cassava pan, as well as woven trays for holding the baked cakes and small conical woven hand covers into which the cook could slip her hand to remove hot bread. It was the village bakehouse. The other houses were in a semicircle facing outwards towards the farm, so that each family had a view uninterrupted by neighbours.

In each house the children lived on one side and the parents on the other. Behind the door were stacked the husband's weapons, his bow and his gun, if he had one. In the eaves were tucked fishing tackle, balls of cotton and other small things. Baulks of wood three inches high, whose upper surface had been slightly hollowed, lay on the ground to serve as bench seats. As usual the fire was in the centre and in the rafters above was hung the dried meat in the smoke. The curing goes on indefinitely so that eventually the meat is the same rich mahogany colour as the rafters.

28

The hammocks are not slung like the Macoushi's. The wife's hammock is slung below the husband's with about a foot between, but this intimacy is rarely exploited and most of the Patamona's sex life is carried on out of doors. The young couple will go off for a day, ostensibly to fish or hunt. They find a waterfall and some large smooth rocks or some other pleasant spot where they play about in the water, make love, fish for a while and then begin again. Only the older couples make love in the houses. Sex to the Patamona is, therefore, a more tastefully conducted affair than among the Macoushi, who, living in one large hut, have little sense of discrimination or privacy.

Labba had cleared his parents out of their house without my knowledge and he said I should use it until my things arrived. But, apart from the inconvenience which I had no intention of causing, I had no wish to sleep in the Patamona houses. Like the Macoushi houses, they smelt vilely of fermented *cassili* and dried meat, mixed with smoke. It took me several more weeks, perhaps six months after I had come into the Indian territory, before I could stomach this pungent mixture. So I suggested that I sleep in the village bakehouse, saying that I found the nights too hot in a building with walls. In fact this was quite untrue, as I now found the mountain night air too cold for comfort. But I preferred cold to smells. They agreed without a murmur. However, I noticed next morning that none of Labba's family had returned to their house, which had been empty all night, presumably in case I might want it.

I asked Labba and his father on the first evening when they thought the porters would arrive. The old man pointed to the distant mountains and explained that when the sun climbed above them, they would come. I estimated that this would be about nine in the morning, as the mountains were well above the horizon line. I said I would like to speak to all who were willing to work for me, at dawn. This was understood, but as we spoke I noticed a deep silence in the houses. Then I saw a head slide swiftly from sight. They were all around, hidden but listening hard. I changed the conversation to the geography of the surrounding country, to learn how the creeks ran and their sources, so that with my map I might be able to fix my position.

It proved impossible, but I was satisfied so long as I kept well in the Pakaraima ranges and close to the tributaries of the big rivers, as that is diamond-bearing country. I went on to ask for the general position of creeks where no one had ever been to prospect for diamonds.

The old man pointed south and spoke half Indian, half English.

"Long time," he said making a hole in the sand with his finger. "Brazilian prospect diamonds. Plenty creek prospect." His information, I reflected, would save me much work as I intended to avoid creeks already worked over. Then Labba broke in, "Plenty creeks. Plenty work. All Patamona man come. All come. Plenty diamond." He seemed confident of discovery and the labour, although I was sure that he knew little about diamonds. They seemed willing to work, but I would make no arrangements until the others came back to the village, as I did not want any man to know the conditions of work except from me personally, so as to avoid the risk of rumours and jealousy. That closed the discussion for the night.

Next day I found a good spot for my camp on the crest of the hill about twenty yards from the village. Labba asked me to trace out the area I should want cleared. I pointed out four trees in a rough square.

"All man work now," said Labba without asking for more details. He seemed to know exactly what was required. He went away and in a few minutes the working party came in the usual file, one behind the other, although it was open ground. Indians rarely walk side by side, but even in file manage to keep a conversation going up and down the line as they pad along in their light, quick steps. They came with axes and knives, but the party of four men and five women and its tools looked puny compared with the job. The hilltop I had chosen was covered in large boulders and massive trees and the undergrowth was dense. The only ones who seemed at home in this spot were the children, who dashed about between everyone's legs, in and out of the matted branches.

30

The party went into the thickets and sat down. I did nothing while they talked for about half an hour, but I was on edge lest this was a sign of unwillingness to work. Finally they got up and dispersed in various directions about the knoll. I heard no sound of axes or of trees falling and went up to the hilltop to see what was going on. I found that they had scattered about and were all digging with their small knives. They were removing all the smallest plants from around the big trees, not cutting them off, but completely removing them by the roots. I called, "Why don't you cut big trees?" The women laughed.

I found Labba and said they seemed to be going about things rather slowly. He said simply:

"*Yapung*—friend—we make good camp." He pointed at the ground. "Small trees very bad."

"Why?" I asked.

"You cut big tree. You put fire. You build camp. But fire burn all tree on top. But small tree seed still good. Rain come. Small tree grow plenty. Grow like big forest quickly under house. House no good."

Later I realised the soundness of Labba's theory. It pays in the jungle to spend an extra day clearing the ground of every single blade of grass before building, if the camp is to be permanent.

So they went on weeding. Each man worked in his own time, resting on his haunches when he felt like it and then starting again. While the work was going on I heard a long note on some kind of horn echoing from the mountains. All the men came down to me. Labba's father was calling out, "People come. People come." The first party of porters were coming in.

"How they make plenty noise? I do not see them," I said.

"*Aragebuza*," said Labba's father, putting his hand to his mouth and blowing. Indians can blow through their gun barrels as if they were trumpets, and the sound carries for miles. To indicate the great distance the old man raised his forefinger and swung it slowly over his head till he pointed to the horizon, while half singing in a high thin voice through his lips "*mojeeeeeeeee*" for about fifteen seconds. It was the first time

31

I had heard this graphic word by which the Indians speak of great distance.

Of course all work ceased at the trumpet sound. The men hurried off to help the first party of porters coming in; the women put their pots on the fire and started boiling dried meat, and the children ran after the men to meet their fathers. But there was no interest in the arrival of the men, although the women got up from their cooking pots occasionally to look down the trail. Within the next hour three porters appeared through the waving cassava, the first party from the original riverside camp. They were puffing with fatigue, their hair plastered down and their bodies greasy and wet. They hardly spoke and, after waiting while their wives undid their *warishi* straps, they straightened up, stretching their necks while they held the edges of their *warishis* for support. I asked when the next lot would come. Again the finger raising and the soft whine, "*mojeeeeeeeee*". They would come when the sun went down, they said.

I told Labba and his father they should unpack the *warishis* and let the men eat and rest; but they did not eat at once. They talked to their wives and then went down to the creek where they threw themselves in the cold water. The children followed them and the three-year-olds, I noticed, were like fishes, quite as good swimmers as their elders.

My tarpaulins had arrived in one of the baskets as well as my personal kit, but no foodstuffs, so I still faced more cassava and dried meat. But there would come a day when I would no longer have the taste for tinned meats. Far better, I discovered, is a leg of fresh-killed meat, roasted on the spit with a rock for table and chair and a sharp knife for cutlery. It was still not late in the day, about three in the afternoon, but work for that day, I could see, was over. The arrival of the porters had broken the spell which the men and women had woven on the knoll that morning, and all Labba's fine resolutions had vanished without a ripple on his conscience. But it would be wrong to underestimate the Indian capacity for sweat and toil. I had begun to see it in the marathon march of the porters for eight days through

32

jungle, mountains and rain with heavy loads on their backs. They still had another cache to lift which meant marching back that day. The only easement these men had was to take the strain of the full load on their head-bands on the march, while they slipped the shoulder-straps away from the bruises to a new position.

When the porters had come up from the stream and eaten, they said they would not wait till next morning but return to pick up the last load that evening at sundown. Labba's father at once piped up and said he would go too to help them. He disappeared for a moment and came back with his *warishi*. It was the biggest I had ever seen and would hold, I estimated, about two hundred pounds easily. He was deadly serious and no one laughed at him, although it was plain that he could not take even a small load for long. They had forty minutes of daylight in hand and it would take them three hours to return to their last camp.

The women went out and cut sticks from a sappy tree of such moisture that the wood would not burn for several minutes even in the heart of a hot fire, and split them at the top and inserted iowa wax. These torches light up the forest for about fifty yards around, and with them the party set off. The old man could hardly walk down the hill and the young men helped him by holding his arms. Almost as soon as they had gone the other party came in. As Labba had gone too I had a chance to talk freely with the others after they had bathed and eaten. The supplies were stacked in the cassava hut. I asked the four porters to come with their bowls so that I could pay them at once with salt and sugar. When the party arrived their families were there too: I was expected not only to feed the nine men I had hired but also their dependents.

CHAPTER THREE

Village Days

In the next two days work started again in the clearing for my camp. All the seedlings and weeds were heaped and burned and then they were ready to tackle the big trees. They looked for the trees with most creepers, which are usually entangled with many of their neighbours. This scouting took some time, so that by the end of it the men had a clear idea of how the vines led from one tree to another. Again I began to feel impatient. Then they started cutting with their axes, but only three trees were chosen out of the whole area. These were the key trees: as they came crashing to earth their connecting vines brought all the others with them.

Then, after a day for the tangled mass of vines and trees to dry, the men started cutting the vines and small branches. They finished in half a day, leaving only the bare trunks of the big trees on the site, cleared for a fire to race through them. They put iowa gum here and there and lit a big fire; when it was well alight they ran about with firebrands lighting the gum, looking for split trees and thrusting fire into the gaps. The trees eventually took hold like coal and burned with great heat for two days, leaving only a few charred hunks which were removed, after cooling in the night mist, by a party with pole levers.

I made a small model with twigs and leaves to show them that I wanted my house to have a floor. They could not understand this and shook their heads. Eventually they grasped that I did not want anything complicated: round poles laid close together, I said, would do. They set to work collecting materials. I noticed that no measurements had been taken whatever, but despite this all the poles were cut to size in the jungle by the individual axemen. Then they called me into the jungle and I found them standing over a great tree they had felled, which they were beating up and down its length with the backs of their axes.

"What you making?" I asked in my halting Patamona.

"Take skin from tree and make house," they said. This was to be the floor. They slit round the trunk and the bark came off in large strips which they carted off to the house. The women were fixing the rafters and I saw that none of the poles was either too short or too long: although the dimensions were strange, their judgment by eye had been as exact as if they had used rulers, set squares and plumb lines. I wondered if civilised man does not make too much of a fetish of his instruments.

I felt it was useless for me to give any more instructions, so I left them to it. The work speeded up. By the time the bark started coming in, the women had the base ready, so that it could be laid while it was still moist and flexible: if left to dry it would have cracked. On top of the ends of the bark strips

35

they lashed thin laths of wood, so that the floor, although humped in places, was springy to the feet like a bed, quite strong and without creaks.

The thatching had to come from a particular lily found only in the mountains, so as a temporary measure I threw my tarpaulins over the frame, while a party went out. As the leaves came in the thatchers started from the ridgepole and worked downwards. So within a week my sixteen-foot-square house was complete in its spotless clearing on the top of the hill. It seemed to me to be a good start among the Patamona. As a special treat I handed out flour and they invented a new recipe and made it into a soup, despite my explanation that flour was for making bread. I had mixed the flour in water and they had tasted the mixture in its raw state, which, being salty, they liked, and so they just boiled this until starchy. Eventually I took a liking to it, although I found that the addition of a little sugar was an improvement.

In the following twelve days all my supplies came in and I felt that I should start at once on serious prospecting. The whole project depended on the length of time that I could last on my supplies and, having been so long with the Macoushi, they were depleted. I estimated that, taking into account the feeding of the Indians, I had only another eight weeks' stock left. Then I considered my equipment and the task. I knew that I could not tap the deep diamond-bearing gravel as the dry season had not started: when the sand covering the deep gravel is damp there is a great danger of the walls of the shafts caving in, despite shoring. I was right in the deep gravel region, in the upper stretches of the main creeks; lower down, where the creeks slope more gently, the gravel spreads out to no more than a foot or a few inches thick. But higher up also, in the small tributaries, the gravel is shallow. So to the small tributaries I would go.

I had learnt that the Brazilian method of sieving was the quickest, and I had chosen my equipment for it. This consisted of some rolls of fine mesh of different gauges and some plywood sheets as well as shovels, spades, hoes and mattocks. During the

36

next two days, with the help of the Indians, I made the sieves. In the Brazilian method there are three of them, saucer-shaped and so made as to fit inside each other with a gap of an inch between each, with the finest at the bottom. At the creek bank the gravel is dug out and thrown into the top sieve, which is half submerged. With a pumping action the water forces through mesh and sends the finer stuff through to the next sieve. After a quick look for big stones the upper sieve is whipped out and emptied. The second sieve is then tried; so on down the creek. Nothing could be simpler: the whole kit could be strapped on the back. It was the favoured method of the old Brazilian prospectors, the pork-knockers.

Fifty years ago was the heyday of the pork-knockers. They took with them a sack of pickled pork to last a year, and they went in "knocking" the gravel here and there on the outskirts of the jungle. Consequently they did not meet the Indians in the hinterland who were feared as strange and savage peoples. The privations of the jungle were enough to kill off many a pork-knocker, without the hostility of the Indians. As a result of this surface scratching, there are still great virgin strands of diamond-bearing gravel. The companies work the rivers, but good land also lies in Indian country, far from transport and civilisation, which distance alone keeps almost impregnable. I hoped that I might succeed where others had failed because of my good relations with the Indians and by use of the simple pork-knocking method.

In the evening, after making the sieves, I explained that I wanted them to take me to the small creeks. Next morning the children were up early as usual, out in the jungle fringe with their blowpipes to shoot early feeding birds, especially the Barbary doves, canaries and the corn birds which feed mostly in the sand. It was chilly as seven of us collected for the expedition. The men did not take their weapons, carrying instead the shovels and sieves, but I took my gun, a habit I kept as I did not have the Indian skill for improvising quick defence. If an Indian is alone and far from camp and finds himself near some large, dangerous animal he will first trace its tracks. If they lead straight across country all is well and he leaves it alone, but if the tracks circle about, indicating that it is in a feeding area, he may make a trap out of vines.

We walked through high jungle over ironstone boulders and stones. This rocky ground forced the trees to send out great roots along the surface, some of them in the upright spine form. The vine entanglements were vile, but unfortunately it was not safe to cut them as the trees there depended greatly on them for support. We had to burrow through the undergrowth for about three hours before reaching a sandy stretch. Here the men halted.

I was not sure of the ground as I could see no water and no defined course in the sand. "We away from the creeks," I said to Labba. "No," he said, pointing at lilies growing in the sand. "Water comes this way." Then I noticed that no tree was standing where the lilies meandered in a belt through the jungle, like a road of green through an avenue, and I realised that there must have been a watercourse here and that the damp sand below ground watered the lilies.

I decided to cover as much of these waterless creeks in the first day as possible, and started to dig a small, foot-square test-pit. The Indians watched me and I explained that everyone must set to work digging such pits all over the sand to find gravel. Then I sent off two men to find the creek sources. They were away for two hours by which time I and the remaining men had dug forty or fifty holes up and down the sand belt, without once striking gravel: the sand went down either to boulders or clay. I was beginning to lose interest in the area when the two men came walking slowly back. They smiled when they saw me and swept their hands from side to side over the ground saying provocatively: "*Gravelly bra. Gravelly bra!*" They had no need to tell me that I could not find gravel where I stood. I wondered how they knew of our failure. They pointed to the east: the gravel ran that way, they said. The others were amused, but I stood among the rash of tiny pits, sweating and annoyed. How could they know where gravel lay? They had taken no tools for testing. In fact they had only become acquainted with the whole business two hours previously.

However, I followed them. None volunteered information. We walked up the lily belt for about a mile and then branched off through the jungle and over a sandy hillock. There was another belt of lilies below. "How do you know there is gravel here?" I asked. Without replying, one of them cut a thin flexible wand about eight feet long from a hardwood tree, with a fork at the head and the base tapered to a sharp point. He took the rod and struck it in the sand and began to plunge it up and down. In a few seconds he had punched it down into the sand until it could go no further. Then he continued to plunge the wand gently for some seconds. On withdrawing the point he ran his finger along it and showed me scars on the end caused by gravel. My shovels were, henceforth, so much ironmongery to be carried as far as testing was concerned. By the wand method a whole day's shovel-testing could be done in an hour; it was possible to outline the drift of the gravel below and also to register the depth. Mining pits could be planned beforehand.

We spread out and began sounding, each man with his wand. Every time a man struck he called softly, *"Gravelly! Gravelly!"* The sun was going down and there was no time that day to dig any mining pits, but all of us tramped happily home knowing at least that we had found gravel conveniently close to the village. Next day the men began to clear large pits on the best spots marked the day before. During the next two weeks they opened several pits. Most were gravel with strong traces of carbon and mica, which I took as signs of diamond gravel. The Indians agreed and called the traces "diamond *yapungs*—diamond friends." They have considerable knowledge of stones and minerals, knowing in what type of country they will be found. Although we worked hard and kept finding mineral traces we found no diamonds, but I did not give up as all the indications showed that this must be diamond country. But my supplies were running out all the time and I decided that somehow they must be spun out further. Why not a farm of my own? It could be on the Indian pattern and instead of the eternal cassava I would grow a variety of vegetables.

The men came round to my hut in the evening as usual to squat and listen to what I had in mind. I knew by this time that such an attentive circle might indicate politeness but not necessarily co-operation. To induce them to follow a plan I usually made a large stack of flour pancakes, fried till brown. Their weakness for flour was so great that it never seemed to fail, and when their bellies were filled they could be talked into enthusiastic work. So that evening I handed out the pancakes lavishly and they sat munching for an hour in the flicker of my fire, nodding as I talked. My plan was for one party to continue prospecting while I directed another at the farm. At first they were not pleased with the idea of planting strange vegetables, so to start them off I suggested that the first area burnt would be planted with cassava. They were used to cassava and I hoped that once started they would go on with other roots. They agreed, but first we had to find suitable land.

A jungle farm has to be near a creek, sloping gently to prevent flooding in the heavy rains. The ideal is moist, well-drained soil. Near the village the best ground had already been taken so another expedition was arranged to find a farming patch.

Parties went out for the next three days, taking their weapons and hunting as they went. While returning one day, a party found a good spot about four miles from the village on a sand spur jutting from the mountains. They also brought back plenty of fresh meat from eight labbas they had killed. I persuaded them not to barbecue the carcasses, but instead to have them quartered, salted and smoked. After being cured they were hung in the roof of my house where I could keep an eye on them to prevent an orgy of eating and the need to go hunting again soon. I hoped this would ensure steady work on the farm.

When the men had gone to make a temporary camp by my farm site I wandered into the village and saw one of the girls, Amelia—the name of a mountain—beating a lily-like leaf. She was taking great care and continued beating the leaf with a small round stone, without looking up.

"What's wrong?" she asked.

"What you making?"

"Lines for fishing."

40

"How do you do it?"

"Wait and see," she said.

After a few minutes the leaf, which was of the hemp plant, was bruised and limp. Patiently she began picking the green flesh away from the veins with her little finger and nail. Then with a practised movement she used her fingers as a rake to clear the smaller veins and waste away from the main strands. She removed each main strand with meticulous care so that it remained whole; bundled the strands and squatted; lifted a thigh and laid all the strands across it. Taking a few at a time she spun them together, controlling their outer ends in the palm of her other hand. She handed me some.

"You try," she said.

I took the strands and began working them on one of my legs. Immediately the strands caught up in the hairs of my thigh and tore them out. I now saw a further reason for the Indians shaving any hair, of which they have little, from every part of their bodies except their heads. The usual explanation is that it prevents jungle ticks from easily alighting on them. She stopped rolling and laughed helplessly. Then she continued until a long thin line came from her hand. When the line began to bind together she slipped into the ends some more veins from the bundle, and in this way the line gradually lengthened until it was twenty yards long.

"Show me the other things you use for fishing."

Her face froze and she looked at the ground. She would have to take me to the creek to show me the fish traps and to an Indian girl that could only mean an improper rendezvous. No Indian girl can allow a man to make any suggestion to her which involves following him out of the village and I had to give her something in atonement. I slipped away and came back with a piece of red ribbon. I pointed to two or three little children playing and said they should come too.

She melted, smiled and picked up some of her lines. We walked down to the creek where she signalled to me to get into a *curee-ole* before her.

"No," I said, "I will steer so you must get in first."

41

Again she froze and stood where she was, gabbling insulting remarks. I got in at once and she followed. Putting one leg in the canoe she put her other foot to a tree root and pushed the canoe half across the creek. She took out her lines as the canoe drifted lazily, and tied it to a short rod no more than three feet long. Having baited the hook she did not cast the bait into the river and wait but switched the worm into the water and as soon as it began to settle below the surface swung it out and across to the other side. So she allowed the canoe to drift as she switched the worm from side to side, and almost immediately she began pulling in small fish. Nine were caught on the first worm before it was frayed out. Passing a small creek she stopped and pointed.

"There we put traps in the high water."

Indians use traps mainly in the rains. The flood waters encourage swarms of smaller fish to swim in the slacker water of the flooded land where they find grubs and worms. The lines are used chiefly in the dry season and for the larger fish. In the mountains few fish exceed more than eight inches in length: for the larger fish the Indians must descend to the rivers in the lower jungle. One fish from the big rivers, the warak, is particularly prized. It is large and tasty, but has more than appetising value.

The ritual of giving a feast among the Indians depends on enticement. They know their own nature and realise that if a distant village is invited to come for a feast they may dally on the way: if the guests should run across a herd of wild hog on the trip they will forget about the party and hunt the hogs. So food is put out on the hilltops along the trails to tempt the guests onward. When they finally reach the host village they are met by a party waving sticks at them on which are impaled the warak.

The warak have been taken whole and smoked till hard, then stuck on sticks at different angles, forming a row. The host villagers come down at the approach of their guests and strike them lightly with these fish-covered sticks and the guests try to snatch the fish. This lively presentation of titbits is the finest enticement of all, besides showing that the hosts have gone to the trouble of travelling many days to the rivers to ensure a feast worthy of their name.

"Before the river is high," went on Amelia, "we make basket across the little creeks." These barriers are made from the lily leaves woven in the form of a long fence right across the stream, supported by vertical poles in the stream bed. When the water is high the fish swim over the fence. The villagers throw many worms and grubs into the upper reaches, encouraging more fish to follow. After the first rush of the rains the water drains off the parched land quickly. As the water drops almost to the level of the barrier, the villagers jump in the stream, form a line across it and chase the fish farther upstream into the shallows. Here, with hand-nets on poles they scoop the fish into their fish baskets strapped at their waists. The children wait on the bank, calling anxiously for permission to enter the rapidly drying pool, so that they can dig out the fish which have escaped the netting and have burrowed into the mud.

Amelia did not like to say more, for like most Indian women she felt at ease only in the presence of others of her sex and age. She pointed to the way back and said shortly, "*Banabu*—house." We started paddling back upstream. She pointed to the bank.

"Big fishes catch with other trap."

"*Anaik*—how?" I asked.

Every time I spoke in Patamona she smiled. She began speaking rapidly about the other traps but it was difficult for her to explain the technical Patamona words and she gestured. I was puzzled. Impatiently she rolled out of the canoe into the cold water and swam along with one hand directing the canoe to the bank. She clambered out through the mud, turning to face me lest her brief bead apron lift over her rump. Indian women frequently emerge from the water in this way. I held a branch to steady the canoe. At the top she turned and broke off a few sticks and slid back into the water.

"*Mazenga. Mazenga*—watch."

She took the longest stick which had a hooked end and

43

stuck it in the water. The second she stuck in the bank and forced down so that it lay sprung underneath the fork, tied a piece of string to its end and repeated *"Canouit canega"* several times. I remembered that *"canouit"* meant a hook and I nodded. She explained that the hook had to be just below the surface of the water when set. The big fishes feed in the inlets on moonless nights. Amelia left the trap set and began to giggle.

"I show you how fish come to the trap."

She swam off about ten feet and sank to her eyes, taking a good look at the trap. Then she submerged, to reappear at the trap and snatch the line. The rod came out of the hooked end of the upright stick and sprang up snapping her arm to its full extent. She dismantled the trap and we paddled back with the children who had been silent and watchful throughout the demonstration.

The others were standing at the edge and Amelia got out with the same backward scuttling method as before. As usual, the others began to ask (amid laughter), what had been happening. I walked up to my camp and Labba's mother pointed to me.

"You *kapung*. You *kapung*." She meant that it seemed that I wanted to be an Indian. *"Yuwalaknung*—I don't know," I said. I went to my camp and was making some coffee from local beans. When its strong aroma had arisen, I heard feet shuffling in the sand outside. I smelt the villagers and waited. Labba's mother came in and looked in surprise at the black concoction in the pot. She pointed and asked what it was. I told her, "Coffee." I had to repeat the word several times, and showed the grains. It seemed that the bean which has made Brazil famous was unknown to them: if they had seen it in the jungle growing wild they had not made use of it. Eventually she coined in her tongue the word *cappee*.

She drew back and said sadly, "*Yapung*, poison." I remembered that the extraction they use for stunning fish in the rivers has the same strong smell as stewing coffee. To convince her I drank some. The crowd had entered. Their mouths hung open and their widely splayed toes turned up in silent anguish. I offered them some. They began wiping their mouths and spitting around saying repeatedly, "No good. No good." They pointed to the cassili shed, "*Kapung cappee* good," and spat again. To them their early morning drink of cold cassili was better than this. They stood waiting. They never left without receiving a gift although they would not ask for it, so I turned them out some of the favourite fried flour cakes.

This kind of incident, broken by the giggling of the women and the squeak of the hammock ropes, was the normal domestic atmosphere in the village during this time. At night there was no sound except the short bursts of crying from the children and a sigh as someone blew up a fire through a hollow bamboo pipe inserted in the embers as a bellows. The children rarely cried or felt anxious for affection or food as they slept with their mothers and the first complaint was stifled at the breast.

The men returned from my farm patch saying the large trees had been felled and they needed some extra help to start the burning. So I and a large party set out next day. Another children's game was to help in this task. A main fire was started outside the farm site and then each person picked up burning brands to light the area from the centre. The children were allowed to circle the patch lighting their own small blazes. Each person called to the next to say that he had set his piece alight and that he was on the way out. While the fire burned that day and night, the women collected cassava cuttings and banana sucker buds to plant. Before Indians begin planting the hunters go through the ashes looking for animal tracks: the deer in particular is attracted to freshly burnt ashes. This time the hunters reported many deer tracks; Labba's father reckoned they were coming in from the thicker mountain jungle and he pointed out the direction. He showed me the marks and told me that they would plant the corn seed where the tracks entered the clearing. Behind it they would plant the cassavas.

They have no regular method of planting except that they choose the deepest ash, especially the burnt tree trunks. The women formed a line and took cassava cuttings from their *warishis,* crouched with their knives in their right hands and

45

dug a small hole into which they pushed the cutting almost level with the soil, never upright. They went steadily forward planting, directed by the men, who by custom never plant. The man is the hunter and the planner; the woman is the camp follower and toiler.

When the planting was complete the women went back to the village and the men stayed on to make the *wabinis* from which to shoot the big game attracted by the sowing. These are eight-foot-high tripods placed over the animal tracks without breaking a stick or disturbing a leaf. Around the top of the tripod is wound a huge mass of chinak ropes until it forms a seat: on this the hunter sits. About twenty *wabinis* were erected around the farm. Occasionally the deer are intelligent enough to leave no tracks on the edge of newly burnt ground: I have seen them jump a clear eight feet from the jungle fringe into the farm. When this happens the hunters set *wabinis* inside the crop area.

In the first few nights the men did not expect much game as the shoots had not grown and the only attraction was the ash. The greatest effort to stop game is made when the buds first shoot. Three nights after the *wabinis* were set up, I squatted in my own *wabini* hoping for a shot. All the hunters had to be in position before sundown, to ensure that any human smell on the ground would be blown away before dark. Two of the men had *aragebuza* guns and I had my 20-bore repeater; the rest had their bows. Altogether eight of us were in position each night.

As twilight drew on, the skill most required was to hear well and to understand the least crackling of twigs. Not even the rustle of my clothes as I reached for a mosquito at my neck could be tolerated, and I sat in excruciating discomfort as the insects tingled and sucked my blood. All was silent. In the last faintness of dusk I saw the neighbouring hunter gesture slightly with his hand. Something was near me but I could hear and see nothing. The hunter on my other side made no move. Then flame leapt in a long tongue from the next *wabini*, followed by the crash of an *aragebuza*. A piece of burning wad fell through the dark like a firefly. A scrabbling shuffle through the sand showed where something was making its dying steps. No one moved. Silence. We sat the night through and that was the only kill, a small labba. I was disgraced in the morning when they showed me how its tracks had passed within a few feet of my hide.

Another night, when the shoots were bursting in the farm behind, the moon was up till nine: the hour of the deer. Just after nine all of us could hear breaking twigs two hundred yards off in the jungle. It sounded intermittently at five-minute intervals. I felt the others tensing and I pointed to the sound. The next hunter thought the animal was too far off to hear and nodded saying, "*Sali*—deer." He turned around and began telling the others in phonetic whistling. We kept still for an hour. Deer are slow to approach feeding grounds. I could hear whiffs of breathing. I turned to the next man; he held up his hand for silence and whispered, "*Piccani*—a young one." Somehow he knew the deer had an offspring with it. Gradually the animals approached the *wabini* second from my left. I could hear them distinctly now, coming out of the jungle to the edge of the sand. The deer stood for another hour before moving in to feed: she must have smelt some slight human scent.

I could see one of the men slowly raise his legs which hung from his seat and hook them round his *wabini* poles. He was one of the long-bowmen. He had already fixed the arrow and drawn his bow to one side, half behind his back. I listened intently but could hear nothing, and bent and looked under the branches to watch him more clearly. He moved the bow to the front of his body with very slow, smooth movements, and aimed below him; stretched his bow and kept it full out for several minutes, raising his aim. The deer shuffled in the sand and the hunter's aim followed him like a tracking camera. Making his final pull, he fired and the arrow breezed off.

Crashing and tumbling, the deer headed straight into the farm and the young one cried. Silence again and the faint hoarseness of the death rattle. Some of the men had vanished from their *wabinis*. Two more bow shots whirred. The deer made a final dash farther into the farm. Again no sound for several minutes. The men appeared and everyone dismounted from his perch. We formed up and closed in to catch the young one. It stood over the hind legs of its mother. One of the men put down his bow and crept slowly towards it. He dived and clutched its legs. It is unsafe to grab even a young deer round the body; its hooves are as sharp as knives. The bellowing little deer had its legs tied and the men carried it out of the farm. The mother was dragged to the creek nearby, its legs tied together and lowered by them to the stream bed. The meat would be safe till morning, and no smell would attract the deer tigers. In the chill dawn mist we lit a fire and sat round eating hard cassava bread until daybreak.

The mother deer was carried slung on a pole back to a smiling reception at the village. The children crowded round the mother lying on the ground and spoke to it in mock anger, slapping it gently. "No good. No good. You destroy our farm." The elders examined the corpse to see its age and how tender its meat was and slipped the doors of the huts down to the ground as meat cutting boards. I told them that I should like the mother's skin, but Labba asked me for the white scut as a plaything for the children. They would cure it, Labba said, and string it to a long string to hang at a child's back during a dance. The fathers collected such mementos and some children sported several this way at feasts.

Meanwhile the baby was being stroked under the ears by the children, who were picking out the ticks from its hide. The skinning of its mother took place out of its sight. I took the skin back to my camp to nail it out, scrape off the fat and wipe it with paraffin. Then some of the boys came and laughed at my preparations.

"What's wrong this time?" I asked.

"Wait," said one and ran off. He returned with a long slender rod from the yari-yari tree, a thin flexible plant used for fishing rods. The boys spread the skin on the ground and bent the wand around it, tying its ends together; when the skin was attached they released the binding on the rod ends and it sprang out stretching the skin. They said that by this means it could be

48

put out in the sun and carried inside when it rained, but if I nailed it to the walls outside, the alternate sun and rain would spoil it. They spread on it ashes instead of paraffin and left it to cure. The Indians seldom cure any skins except that of the tiger, which makes fine hunting bags.

For the baby deer the girls went out to find tender seeds and nuts, but it did not eat for more than a day. They went on crushing the food and putting it out and, although they explained that it was usual for young captured animals to refuse food, they were anxious. I gave the girls some evaporated milk in a pan. They looked and agreed that it was like milk. I showed the tin but they would not believe that milk comes out of tins. I tried to explain that milk was taken in the big cities and dried. They saw the cow on the label, but it was no good. When they take milk from an animal it spoils in two or three days and this meant my "milk" could not have lasted. They summed it up by saying it was *milik walaie*—near to milk. Scientifically, of course, they were right.

I gave up the argument and tried to feed the little animal. I took a piece of cotton and soaked it in the milk and squeezed it into the deer's mouth. He began to drink it and the children took over and sat around feeding him all day. During the night his bonds were loosened and he was brought into a hut to the warmth of the fire. Next day Labba's mother told me that the baby had not slept all night. She laughed and said it had probably smelt its mother cooking in the pot next to it. This produced fits of giggles and struck me as a typical Indian joke: their sense of humour is nearly always concerned with animals. They will lie for hours on a creek bank dangling food on the surface, watching the antics of fish rising to it. They might note the way a fish arches its back to swallow, and laugh. That evening, hours after, the story will be repeated—"Did you see how the fish arched its back to swallow"—and the laughter will bubble again.

Labba's mother began chewing the nuts laid out for the deer. I asked her why. She lowered her head and fixed her eyes on me with a grunt as if I had been rude. She bent her head and her hair dropped like a veil, while she spat in her hand a pasty ball of chewed nut and popped it in through the side of the baby's mouth. It ate the paste and she prepared more. This went on for hours until she thought the deer satisfied. This pleased me as my milk was saved. For four days the deer remained in her care and it appeared as if she were the foster mother. The children were annoyed, for all wanted a share in ownership, but Labba's two younger sisters were naturally pleased at their mother's success. The other children began screaming and shouting when it was decided that the deer would stay with Labba's family.

All over the village mothers were thumping their off-spring on the back of the head or pulling their ears to quiet them: the usual chastisement. The mothers then took their children to their fathers resting in hammocks. It was explained that their children could no longer play with the deer as it had become the property of the Labbas. The fathers turned and looked at the wall. Still the soft, persistent campaign continued. A father would eventually jump up in exasperation. "All right," he would say, "come with me." Half amused, he was nevertheless on his mettle to find his child something to tame. The men saw the joke of it.

The father left the camp, asking through a doorway if the man of the house was coming too. With a sigh the other rose and took his weapons from behind the door. We were off pet-hunting. We went to the tall jungle where the parakeet and the macaw live. Every tree passed was examined for nests. We looked in the sand also for the blue maam which lays in the sand, and makes a good pet, but we found only its royal blue eggs. We came across a small flight of waracobra —one of the fastest birds on its feet, which seldom flies. They had chicks and we chased after them with the children yelling and caught three. This would have done except that one man had promised his son a parakeet. The waracobra chicks were put in a basket and we went on up the mountain spurs, looking in many nests all of which had only eggs.

We decided to go into the macaw country, the lighter jungle on dry sand where the old trees wither from lack of moisture. The sun struck through the dried, broken branches of the ancient jungle giants and the whole area had a blasted, forlorn look. Most of the tree trunks were punctured by holes where the macaw nested. We threw stones to arouse them. One or two macaws flew out and we could see the young ones stretching their necks from the holes, but they were twenty or thirty feet up the smooth bole.

A man cut some chinak creeper four feet long and tied the ends with a reef knot round the tree and by lifting the rope with his toes gave himself a foothold as he pulled up with his hands. He looked in all the holes, turning himself round on the trunk. He plucked out a chick and came down with its wing held in his lips. He went up again for another and the children were wreathed in smiles, holding their birds close, comparing them and boasting of size and markings on their own. Then we returned to the village now in the grip of a pet craze. Indians usually have one or two pets and are adept at both catching and taming almost any creature, although birds are the favourites. They never cage their pets and give them complete freedom.

The taming is done by the elder girls. They cuddle the bird for hours, stroking it gently and lifting its beak. They never feed it on raw food: food is first half-chewed by the girls and the bird is fed from the girl's mouth. Eventually the bird is taken off its own diet and is made to eat the Indian food of cassava and in effect the Indians replace the mother bird. The chick develops trust and adopts the Indian diet so that it soon no longer desires to return to the jungle, where now it could not easily survive.

Once in this village they were taming an acouri, a creature the size of a rabbit with the same face and hopping gait, but with small pointed ears and golden fur. For many days they fed it on nuts and then cassava bread until it was quite tame. They made a home for it in the camp. It had to be a hollow gourd, as a hole is the acouri's natural lair. One day it ran off and the whole village turned out to search for it. Two days later it came back on its own, and scuttled into the

51

gourd and stayed there in a shivering state of fright. The villagers called it softly but did not touch it. Eventually it came to the entrance and they picked it up. It was bitten and torn and thin. The villagers explained that it had gone back to its own kind who, scenting the human smell it carried, had set upon it. The same thing happened to a powice which had been tamed. It returned with beak marks round its head, which the Indians easily identified as marks of other powice. This often happens to a tamed animal returning to the wild.

They once tamed a wild pig until it was full-grown, which I named Bingo. It developed the habits of a tame dog, standing on its hind legs to them and grunting in the way a dog barks greeting. When it was called by name it would stop its perambulations of the village and snap its teeth together so loudly that the sound could be heard half-a-mile away. It followed me everywhere, walking alongside like the best-trained gun dog. In fact the tamed wild pig is better for a jungle hunter, for wild pigs are ferocious enemies of snakes, and their thick blubbery hide, in which there are few blood vessels, protects then from snake-bite. Their horny snouts and great tusks are formidable weapons against anything on the ground. For this reason the Indians prize tamed pig, especially around their children.

One pet the Indians never have: monkeys. Although they recognise the monkeys as the most sensible of the jungle creatures, once they are tamed and have overcome their shyness they become extremely destructive.

CHAPTER FOUR
The Fishing Trip

It was mid-October, the time to begin preparing for the great feast of the year, the highlight of Patamona life. Distant tribes come in. Marriages are made. A spiritual consciousness descends on them and the routine of hunting is left aside for gossip, love-making, tales of adventure and philosophising. It is the broody season, culminating in the most important event of all: the dancing.

Their approach to this period is subtle and hard to discern, quite unlike the excitement preceding Christmas or Chinese New Year or any of the world's other festivals. At first there is a gradual moody distraction from work; excuses are found for not hunting, yet they cannot make up their minds to start preparations for the feast. Curiously they have no word for the whole season, merely describing it as the time of talking, eating, dancing and so forth.

When I went out prospecting, they followed reluctantly in little groups. I knew all of them were well and I could not understand it. We looked at different creeks but their attention was elsewhere. Catching sight of some huge silver bali trees, one said they would be good for the end of the year—the silver bali is cut out to form enormous bowls to hold the festival *cassili* drink. Others wandered off to feel the texture of various palms to see if they were at the desired ripeness to make flexible skirts and headdresses for the male dancers. The women sought their own ornaments, beads and stones which they strung on necklaces and bands.

I asked myself why, at this season, they sought the silver bali, normally made into canoes, and the palms, usually for fish baskets. The fish were scarce before the heavy rains and we had a large enough fleet of canoes at the landing places. I could see no reason for their behaviour but waited for another day to see if the same restlessness would continue.

I worried during the night. They were sitting out in the open and I could hear my name mentioned several times, but all I could pick up was the occasional word about fish and canoe and hard work. It seemed that they were unable to explain to me what was happening. Yet they thought that I understood and was pretending ignorance, so as to make them work. In fact, of course, the misunderstanding was on my side too. Next morning they looked very sulky when we started off on another trip and I thought I would try to break the atmosphere by offering them some cigarettes. I received the usual smile, but I was disturbed to see that they immediately sank back into their sulks. I wondered what I was doing that was wrong.

At that moment I heard quick footsteps coming down the trail and two children appeared with beautiful birds in their hands, from whose chests stuck darts. I stood up and waited for them to pass. They ran to the other villagers and everyone began to admire the fine feathers. They went on examining them. I thought their interest excessive, as they are accustomed to seeing such things every day of their lives. Then to my amazement I heard one of the men saying they would be good for *"Klismassee atai"*—literally "Christ comes this time." Instead of walking on I sat down on a log and started questioning them. I asked what was wrong. They said they did not know in a way I knew to be a hint that I should be more specific. I called Labba's father, put my hand on his shoulder and asked him to sit down.

"You are an old man and wise to many things," I flattered him. "I am just to you like a son who will listen to your words." He groaned several times and slapped his hand on the ground as a sign to the others to sit. They began to giggle, which is not unusual when something serious is in the air. He tried his best to speak the English I had taught him, to ensure I understood, although I could by now speak their language reasonably well.

"*Yapung*, all people worry. Buck man *banabu*, no meat, no fish. Big rain come soon. Big feast come soon. Buck man worry."

I asked him what he wanted me to do. He turned with a mild apologetic expression.

"All man no work," shaking his head. "All man no work. Time come we hunt. We fish plenty. All woman make drink. Klismas come. Big feast."

I broke in to ask where they got the word Christmas from. Amou, one of the more intelligent ones, became very grave. "*Kapung* know," he said to me, pointing to the sky. "*Kapung* God—Indian God. Me know. All man know. Klise, Klise." Probably the name of Christ had filtered through from casual encounters with frontier prospectors.

I told them at once that they must of course stop work and get their fish and all else required. They smiled with relief and called me a good man: a rare compliment. They asked

55

me to come with them when they went down to the big rivers. This discussion changed the atmosphere completely; the village was happy once more. All their half-secret scheming was revealed to me; that the women had been busy in the farms without my knowledge, and that the hunters had taken time off to track animals.

They started non-stop work, felling the silver bali trees. The children collected as many birds as they could shoot, of any kind so long as the feathers were fine. Others kept watch for eagles to be shot by the men: the talons are hung round the neck and shoulders to signify strength. The gourds, growing on vines in the farms, were cut, hollowed and strung on poles to dry, then carefully scraped inside once more and soaked in the river, to swell the skins and prevent leakage through the pores. All other available vessels were also collected for the forthcoming drinking bouts.

Large hooks and fishing lines were gathered from the caves of the houses for the river trip. From the bakehouse, smoke blew over the roofs day and night. I could smell the special rations for the hunting party being prepared, and hear the shuffle of the *aki-yai*, the cassava grater, and accompanying bursts of song. Others drew *cassili* from the first of the cassava harvest, which would go with the hunters. An enormous amount of work had to be done and I could not believe they could have all ready by the feast.

The excitement kept them talking at night, but I slept as much as I could with the prospect of the long trip with strenuous fishing at the end of it. Finally the day came and I was aroused at about four in the morning, before dawn. Both *curee-oles* were packed and I could see iowa gum torches flickering round them as men saw that all was secure. I hurriedly packed my twenty-five-pound pack with tinned meats, coffee, cigarettes and many rounds of ammunition. I told the others to look after my camp, especially to keep the children away: I did not worry about theft but visualised a child setting the place alight by mistake. They promised that they would

56

thump the children and started right then to bang all in sight on the back of the neck.

The whole village crowded round the landing, huddling round the feeble warmth of the torches. The party of three women and five men, including myself, packed into the spaces between the stacked stores in the boats. The cassava bread was in the bows, covered with huge lily leaves, and the gourds of liquor amidships, their mouths stoppered by tight coils of bush rope. Those on shore pushed us into mid-stream. One called, "Don't let the fish pull you in. You will look silly as bait."

"I would be the fish then. When I came back you would have to eat me," came the reply.

"Not me, you are too fat, bloated one." This referred to the Indian distaste for fatty meat.

Amid laughter, we paddled off slowly in the heavily laden *curee-oles* through the extreme chill of the mist in the creek. Looking back I could still see the glare of the torches and the black figures on the bank. Then the trees intervened and we were left to ourselves and the silence of the creek. Labba was there with me and Amou and three younger boys. Labba's mother was the senior among two younger wives, called by them *nopuiks*, skilled in fishing, whose husbands had gone hunting. Most of the party crouched for warmth and there was not much talk.

As dawn broke I saw new country: dense jungle, here and there broken at the banks where tapirs had made trails to the water. It smelt strongly of decayed vegetation as the nearby swamps were drying out. There was also a cloying smell of plum and many balata trees in fruit, on which myriads of birds feasted noisily. Just then one of the women pointed out the balata fruit, peach coloured, the shape and size of a small chipolata sausage, and told me that it is good to eat. Indians usually favour any edible fruit which is sweet and fleshy.

We drifted slowly with the current until about seven-thirty, when we began eating the cassava bread and drinking

57

cold cassili. Some took two hours to finish, picking slowly
at their food, dipping their bread in the river to soften it.
That day we travelled through shallows for over thirty miles,
stopping many times to cut fallen trees and to drag the canoes
over sandbanks, first scraping away the sand with bare hands.
There was some danger from sharp submerged stones, although
there was no fear of the electric eel or the piranha fish, as these
frequent only the lower rivers and deep water. Alligators
slumbered everywhere, but they rarely attack unless disturbed.
Crocodiles are more aggressive.

Dusk fell more quickly than usual as we were hemmed in
by thick jungle and nearby mountains. At six-thirty our first
day's trip was over, and the men became alert for a suitable
camping spot. They were very particular, seeking open places
where palms were plentiful. We pulled in eventually and Amou
moved up the centre of the boat slowly and surely. As the
boat touched the bank he sank his broad feet into the mud
and hauled his stocky figure, fair for an Indian, upwards,
grunting slightly with effort, saying, "Akay, Akay—I am too
heavy for this work." Everyone began calling on him to be quick
to find a site as darkness was falling. We could hear him
rustling in the undergrowth, and in a few seconds he shouted
that he had found a good spot, although there were many
thorns around.

We were so tired that no one protested. Both *curee-oles*
drew together and two men held the gunwales of each; the
others sat still as one man unloaded carefully to prevent a
capsize of the heavily laden craft. I was so cramped after hours
of sitting in one position that I had to hold the shoulder of
a boy to get out. I asked Labba to get some twigs to start a
fire, and he suggested cutting greenwood to make the fire last. I
lit some iowa wax and the fire was soon blazing cheerfully.

Fires are almost symbolic of comfort to an Indian. They
light them everywhere, even when it is warm; and now everyone's spirits rose. As usual, the first task was to sling the
hammocks. The women slept in their own circle round their
own fire, talking quietly among themselves. Everyone was soon

58

asleep, without any preparation to keep the fire going, as we were so tired.

Next dawn a fair day rose and it was warm early, and I expected it to be hot later. Amou told me that we had only about five or six more turnings in the creek before we would have to abandon the boats and travel on foot. Two miles farther on we came into a shallow tributary and the steersmen called for fast paddling to run the boats well up on the sandy shore. The boats' keels hissed over the sand and Labba jumped out to pull the boat further on. Then he scampered back, holding up his hand for silence.

"*Kai-cushi. Kai-cushi*," he whispered—"Tiger."

The men got out carefully and examined the pad marks in the sand. We prepared for action, but after tracking forward Labba put his bow down and pointed through the thickets to an empty lair. The Indians went boldly forward to measure the size of it. An old head of a deer lay to one side and the decaying head of a tapir.

"*Kai-cushi* big. No trouble now. He feed on tapir," said Labba.

"Why not eat the head?" I asked.

"No, head last thing he eat."

I went to pick up the antlers, but Labba dissuaded me from touching anything, and we left quickly and returned to the stores and the women and set off overland, climbing about 1,600 feet through a rocky scene with great boulders and trees. Here and there the rocks were large enough to keep the trees apart and form a vent through which the sunlight poured. We had not eaten and pushed on at the highest Indian speed, so that I could hardly keep up as they twisted and sprang through the undergrowth, over sharp rocks, slippery patches and across crevasses. The only sound was the flap of my rubber boots. We passed good game without giving it a second thought, and continued for hours without respite. By sunset we must have covered fifteen miles over country through which, had I been alone, I might have made six with difficulty.

We had crossed the border of British Guiana and were

coming into the region of the Kaieteur Falls, said to be the highest sheer fall of water in the world: 822 feet. The Patamona call them "Old Man's Fall." Long ago these Indians took their old men, who could no longer hunt or work, with all their belongings, in a *curee-ole* to the falls. After a solemn farewell ceremony they were reverently placed comfortably in their canoes and guided into midstream, from where they went over the falls. Although this seems callous, it is to the victim more fearful than painful, as it is certain that consciousness slips away long before reaching the bottom of such a torrent of water. But after seeing these enormous falls I realised that for the old men to go through the ceremony they must have had above all a great courage and a firm belief in the rightness of their dramatic end.

The fishing grounds were below the falls and that night we camped in the mountains on the banks of the Potaro River. Ahead I could see endless boiling rapids and cruel rocky outcrops. It was wild country, the jungle opening out and petering away. The women went along the banks and caught a few fish for our supper, flat and only about six inches long. They rubbed them on a smooth stone until the scales came off; then, after washing them, threw them into a small Indian pot and boiled them whole; that was our meal.

Next morning we pushed on through thick jungle over rough ground. To avoid the thickest undergrowth by the river bank, we skipped from rock to rock. The rocks were ironstone, jagged and sharp, and my bare feet were soon cut and torn—I had chosen to walk barefoot like the Patamona as I found it gave me a better grip. They seemed to find no difficulty in swinging along quickly with their loaded *warishis*. As the roar of the river increased, their voices rose in excitement above their usual soft tones. Amou would break off and turn to me to call "*Aekee bemang?*—Do your feet hurt?"

The young *nopuiks* laughed at consideration which they would never have given to each other. They continued, pointing out the different rocks below, the quartz and sandstone, wholly absorbed in this evidence of new country and paying no attention to familiar fruits or animals.

"How beautiful that stone is," one said. She picked up a smooth stone and popped it in her mouth to feel the smoothness. At a silent pool they all stopped and admired it.

"That stone shines like a diamond."

"Look at that shimmer like gold."

The other *nopuik* spat out her stone into her palm, looked at it and slipped it back into her mouth. So she went on, throwing it out and feeling it in her mouth again. They strode like young Amazons, their legs as muscular as men's. Above their waists, the fat bulged over their skirt strings, which are often kept at the same tension from youth and gradually cut into the flesh. They never walked directly in front of me, always to one side, a sign of reticence customary before a stranger.

At another pool they watched a ripple on the surface and discussed what kind of fish made it. One said it was a warak, another pointed to bubbles rising. Probably he has seen us, she said. He wants to frighten us. She must have remembered that electric eels have this habit, although there are none in this region. Here, in the swift-flowing river there were no dangers, and one could safely plunge into any pool. Below the waterfall, where the river straightened out and ran slowly to the sea, all the horrors of piranha fish and electric eels returned. The women had become sufficiently accustomed to me to address me directly, first switching their heads to half cover their faces with their long hair, and we talked of the beauty around. The water sparkled under the sun and the foam bubbled among the rocks. Flowers spread over the bank as the jungle thinned out, and ferns, such as grew below their village, sprang out of crevices. Suddenly they all stopped and pointed out a red bird with a round head and flowing plumage, the cock-of-the-rock, now rare in the jungle. Amou explained the scarcity by swinging his arm to indicate many moons and then said *"Mojeeeee"* to indicate long ago. These birds, he said, once roamed the

61

jungle in large flocks but were now to be seen only in ones and twos. He said that Indians never shot them, in the hope that they would multiply again, although it was difficult to stop the children, who fired at anything in sight when learning to use weapons. The older Indians never shoot for amusement and to them the cock-of-the-rock, like all in the jungle, is part of their lives.

Eventually we reached their boats, which they leave at this place on loan to a nearby related tribe. They were reluctant to do anything to indicate that their loan was conditional, and did not want to leave trace of having used them, so the raising of the boats was done furtively. The boats lay below the water filled with stones and moored by chinak ropes in the usual way. Amou dived down and I could see him below the surface unloading the ballast and placing it carefully to one side so that it could be found again. The men would not ease their task by cutting levers, lest signs of their presence was left. I watched to learn their ways, the only sure way of gaining their confidence.

We fitted thwarts in the boats and paddled out into mid-stream, the men in one boat and the women in a smaller craft behind. Only the steersman had any work, as the swift current took us quickly along for about fifty miles. Here and there we had to work carefully through rapids. They said they would stop about half a mile above the falls themselves. It struck me at the time that this was cutting it a bit fine, as the current was already powerful; I visualised the immense drop of water ahead and suggested that we stop at least four bends of the river from the falls. They told me not to be afraid and seemed unconcerned at the danger ahead.

At a mile from the falls I tied my pack to the boat and stripped in case I had to make a jump for it. The roar of the falls filled the air ominously. I told the steersman to head into the bank as we hurtled on in midstream. The water bulged up from the banks to the centre and dipped and rose in long waves. Again they refused to take my advice. They said that it would mean death to go near the banks, where the

smallest stick might rip out the bottom of the boat. I asked
how many more bends there were, and they replied, two more.
They would swing in to the landing place half-way through
the second bend. It seemed mad to take such a risk and I
eased my way over the *warishis* into the stern of the boat and
took the paddle. The boy looked at me with rude hate and
sulked. The others laughed and accused me of fear. I said I
only wanted to learn how to steer, but as soon as I was in
position I brought the bow over and headed towards the bank.

The speed of the boat was so great that I could hardly
control it. Their warning proved correct for, as we raced towards
the bank, I saw immense whirlpools, their centres two or three
feet below the surface. As the boat hit the first it stopped as if
flung against the end of a rope, then lurched into the centre
and began to spin and shudder violently. Still apparently un-
daunted, but now serious, the men called at me to see what
trouble we were in, but they did nothing to remedy our
situation.

I patted Amou on the shoulder. "I am not so good as an
Indian," I confessed. In that wild scene, the boat spinning, the
falls roaring ahead, great trees on the banks whipping in and
out of the tossing water and jagged rocks flinging the racing
water in spouts through which rainbows glittered, I knew that
I had almost lost my head. Amou looked at me intently for
some seconds, then smiled slowly.

"Me make good," he said, "me teach you good."

He took the paddle and they all bent to the task. It took
us a good ten minutes of hard paddling to free the boat from
the whirlpool, which fortunately did not move downstream
as it was held in an orbit near the bank in cross-currents and
backwash. As we paddled hard, the boat began to take water
and one man started to bail. The next boat, meanwhile, had
gone on ahead and was out of sight. I tried to imagine what
the old men must have felt as they went on alone on that vast
stream, heading for the lip of water to see the country far below
before the drop. It seemed to me that the scene was so terrifying,
so much more gigantic than normal experience, real or imagi-

nary, that a man might easily be numbed into a kind of hypnotised state before actually reaching the lip of the falls.

Once more we headed into midstream, the paddlers adding to the speed of the current so that we gathered a great momentum. Their reasoning, as usual, was sound. By gathering speed in the centre they were able at the right moment to shoot the boat across the current and into the bank. Without such speed we might have been unable to drive out of the river into the shallows before the fall. The landing place was an undercut cave where the boats lay peacefully, and after unloading, the Indians let the boat out on ropes so that it stood away from bumping.

After lighting a fire and eating some farine, we set off on foot on the three-mile descent to below the falls, where we intended to fish. The river runs across a plateau before the falls, but first we had to climb a shoulder on the side of it, away from the falls. The path had been cut by geologists and was about four feet wide with a sheer drop on the outer side of the plateau. Occasionally I could see the bottom of the cliff about a hundred feet below; at other times there was only a bank of mist. This is a favourite tourist area, but visitors rarely see the Indians coming down to fish. If strangers should approach the Indians from the mountains, they will turn their faces to the cliff and let the strangers pass and then examine them from head to foot and note every detail.

At the top of the path, level with the falls, a great plain of pebbles stretched away. The river was visible behind for about fifteen miles and more than sixty miles away rose the blue ridges of the Pakaraimas, from where we had come. The Indians stood for many minutes looking back, the *nopuiks* showing the greatest interest, saying that behind those hills lay their houses. Labba's mother had seen all this before, but the *nopuiks* and the boys had never been so far from home. We spread out and walked for twenty minutes across the desolate plateau, then made the descent, having to pass at times beneath upturned slabs of stone which leant against each other, forming large caves. Inside them were blood-sucking

64

vampire bats, some of which had a wing span of about eighteen inches. The Indians hurried through this murky darkness although they were unconcerned at the bats, being only afraid of them should they have to sleep within their reach. Having less practice than they, I was frequently bruised when crawling through the narrow exits.

I had been so badly shaken, cut and bruised by the trip that I now tried as hard as I could to adopt their methods, which were obviously so suitable to the country. As we clambered down they never looked far ahead, keeping all their attention to the ground a few feet in front of their feet to pick the smooth stones among the sharp ones. All seemed to put their feet exactly in the footsteps of those in front.

At the foot of the descent the scene again became attractive, with ferns, flowers and mineral springs sprouting from rocky spurs. As in everything, the Indians chose the quickest method of having a drink, taking a leaf and forming a cocked hat to act as a spout and shooting the water into their mouths. We crossed a small bridge built by the government over a ravine, to the foot of which I descended, in order to hear beneath it the rumbling of an underground stream and feel the faint vibration of the ground. The whole region had, presumably, been thrown up in a primeval disturbance and been left as a wild jagged place, over and under which the water roared.

We went through pleasant woods, more open than jungle and we reached the bottom. "Plenty cashew," said a *nopuik* and sprang up the tree, sat on a branch and began eating the nuts. The others followed suit, and soon all of them were in the trees. There were some shelters left by other Indians, so we had no need to make camp. It was quite cold under the shadow of the waterfall and its spray dampened everything, although it was itself out of sight round some bluffs. The sand was infested with jigger fleas, that burrow into the foot and lay eggs which gradually swell until the nest has to be excised. This the Indians usually do carefully with a thorn and then eat the whole lot, an unpleasant method which they justify on the grounds that it is a certain way of reducing the number of jiggers.

We wasted no time in setting about fifteen spring-rod fish traps like those Amelia had shown me, over a mile along the bank. To reach them easily the Indians made temporary one-man canoes called woodskins, made from the flexible bark of a tree. First they pick a smooth unblemished bole with twelve feet or so of smooth bark and beat round the base and the top and up the centre line so that eventually the sheet of bark springs away from the wood. Then they cut lengths in half and divide them lengthwise, so leaving four strips of bark which immediately roll up into troughs. They incise the ends for a few inches and bend the flaps so formed over each other, fastening them with thin chinaks through punched holes. This raises the ends, which are not watertight, and they ride clear of the water when the woodskin is loaded. To keep the sides apart they insert stretchers and leave the wood-skin in the sun to harden round them. Handling a woodskin requires much practice and at first I found that I could not get into one without sinking it. The freeboard is only a few inches and it has to be entered slowly with the hands on the sides so that the ends gradually flex up clear of the water while it is kept in exact balance. But an Indian can travel for hundreds of miles through rapids in a woodskin. Through rough water he ceases paddling and lets the craft ride, the water carrying it safely through the rocks, requiring only an occasional flick of the paddle.

Before evening the woodskins were ready and Labba said there would have to be a night watch by one man in a wood-skin up and down the fish traps. I had a better idea, but I would not explain it to them all at once. Indians respect an explanation which takes some time to demonstrate, saying to a brief piece of advice that if it could be thought of so quickly it could have come to anyone and must therefore be useless. Their leadership depends not on a recognised authority but on anyone who displays momentary initiative. Even a small boy may guide them so long as he talks sense. As soon as the wise one of the moment falters, his leadership is rejected and, possibly, all his other ideas, including those which had gone before.

I searched in my pack and brought out some empty tins, collected others left by tourists and put in them some small stones. They followed me down the line of rods, eager to know what I intended. They forgot my strangeness and brushed against me, leaning over to watch me tie them to the rods and eagerly handing me lengths of chinak. I felt that I was becoming accepted among them. A *nopuik* suggested that the reflection of the tin in the moonlight would attract the fish. Another disagreed, saying that the fish should not be distracted from the bait. Still mystified, they followed me back to the camp fire, where we sat. I told them they must be quiet and put no watch that night. Amou complained that crocodiles would eat any fish caught. I persuaded them to wait, and after whispering and munching cassava for about an hour I heard three clattering notes from the tins. Without moving they said that people were coming. I said no, the fish were coming. Light dawned and they were all smiles and sighs. They laughed for ten minutes.

"You good medicine," said one.

"You *pi-eye warawak*—a wise one."

It is by consistently displaying far-sightedness that their wise men, philosophers, or witch doctors, as they might be called, are chosen. However, I had not graduated to that level. We ran to the lines and picked up three fish. When we had collected about four hundred pounds of fish, they began smoking them whole. Again I showed them a better way, making them gut the fish and split them down the centre so that they dried more quickly. They were annoyed at first at the idea of throwing away the guts and eyes, which I knew would rapidly rot the fish.

We made extra *warishis*. I showed them how they could avoid a double trip up the mountain, by suspending them from poles on the shoulders of the men. We retraced our steps up the mountain, hurrying along and eating from the

67

fish as we went. Here and there we broke off to shoot tapir. At the landing place where we had left the canoes they took a day's rest before the return journey against the current and the slope of the hills. As the moon rose that night, Amou told me there was an old trail leading to the actual foot of the falls where the Patamona and the Wai-Wai used to fish. He said he might be able to find it although it was overgrown. I gave him some cigarettes to keep the thought with him.

I had been hoping to see the fall at close quarters but had not wished to press them to such an expedition while they were keen to return home. Amou, Labba and I set off next day, the holiday, and Labba picked out the trail, untrodden for many years. He looked for signs such as grass shorter than the rest, rubber trees which had grown again from a cut base, showing where a line had been slashed through the undergrowth. We had to descend through crevasses by leaning our backs and elbows against one side and levering down by our knees and feet on the other. Some drops we took on chinaks. At the bottom enormous boulders and mud lay in wild confusion.

Their hope was to find old traces of their tribe, but it seemed hopeless as the water had probably wiped them out. Labba and Amou went in short bursts, first looking carefully ahead, into caves and across crevasses, and then jumping and slithering swiftly onward. The fall sounded louder, thundering heavily; spray filled the air and stung our faces. It was impossible in the dimness of the spray to see the curve of the fall. We edged along over rocks above jet black water a dozen feet below. Some rocks were great jagged splinters which had fallen from above. I came round one of these and there was the fall.

I was a hundred yards from it. I seemed to be looking straight up at a great mass of water that bellowed and crashed down from the sky like a vast river in rapids turned up on end. The noise was intense and numbing. At the foot, the water exploded and boiled up in fifteen-foot waves, topped with thick foam. We could no longer shout and had to make signs.

68

Amou and Labba shivered in the cold. In the cracked rock around us, red snakes wound in and out. I signalled to go on and we clambered on to the side of the fall. Fortunately the spray seemed to be heaviest in the centre and on the side away from us, so that we were able to continue on our course.

We passed round the side of the fall and entered a vast grotto behind the water like an immense dim cathedral, hung with rocks and stalactites. The water was twenty feet below and shot out in wavering gushes from above, and I realised later that a chance gush could have swept us down. From the back of the chamber to the fall was about fifty yards. The sound diminished as the fall insulated its own sound. We threw stones at snakes in our way and climbed over boulders. Then I heard a sudden swelling noise, similar to water but drier. Amou pointed upward and there, behind the falls, flew thousands of swallows. We recognised the stench of their droppings. Then we saw bats and many other kinds of small life including the large edible frog. "*Waluk mak*," I said to them. "No good," said Labba, and screwed up his face in disgust, for living in perpetual gloom had changed the colour of the frogs to light grey instead of glistening black. We were walking along about five feet below high water mark and I thought that when the river was low the water would come down so close to the face that it would be impossible to go behind it. In full flood the water would boil up and half fill the grotto, so this expedition could only be possible at half flood.

As we went farther I heard strange rumbling sounds and I could not decide whether it was the echo of the fall or another fall underground. We came to a bluff and the path of boulders narrowed. It was almost dark. I took off my shirt to prevent its catching and told them to wait while I went into the centre of the back of the falls. I came round the corner and stood for some time looking around trying to see what kind of rocks lay there. There was granite, but suddenly I saw some strips of mica and then quartz. This was a sign of gold. I picked up a large stone and, sure enough, its surface was speckled with gold, and the rock on which I sat showed the same signs. I imagine there is a reef running through there somewhere, but as this is a national park it is impossible to work it; besides there is the difficulty of operating behind the fall.

There was no sign of life in the innermost hall and I imagined that it would be dangerous to go farther. When I rejoined Amou and Labba they asked me if I had seen the evil spirits which lived there. I said nothing and felt satisfied with my expedition.

We climbed slowly back, each with his own thoughts. On reaching camp we faced hard work. It had taken us only a day to come down the river from where the boats had been hidden, but now it would take us four back-breaking days to paddle upstream, rarely pausing for food and going from dawn to sunset. The first two miles were the worst and we had to avoid the whirlpools, as we made our way up close to the bank. Higher up we met rapids which, on the way down, I had hardly noticed.

We went through the rapids in "monkey jumps." This is different from portage as it is done without leaving the river. The main thing is for the boat to face the stream. It is edged up close to the rapid, all continuing to paddle although the boat is now stationary. The bow and stern men use their paddles sideways and the boat slides over to a convenient rock. One man jumps and holds the boat heading into the stream. Everyone gets out and unloads the boat. Long ropes are led forward to the head of the rocks where members of the crew stand. The empty boat is hauled forward and through the rapid and all load up again.

We did this three times. The last seemed to be as easy as the rest, but as we reached the centre the boat began to sheer about wildly and take water. For the first time the men were worried. All the *warishis* were lifted on to the gunwale to prevent the fish being soaked. The men were shouting. We paddled steadily and we seemed to be regaining control when one of the boys, Peta, lifting his *warishi*, fell

70

over the side and was swiftly swept away. I called on the steersman to turn the boat, but they took no notice and paddled on without showing any concern. Peta reappeared from time to time spinning between rocks and hurtling away from us. He let himself go for a long way and then dived below the surface and swam ashore. The men knew, better than I, his capabilities. He had done the right thing, which is not to struggle, as the water takes a relaxed body safely between dangers and to struggle on the surface is to risk being dashed on a rock or being drowned. Even in whirlpools it is better to go down and try to break out below the surface where turbulence is less. As Peta displayed this form of skill in the boiling water, I went through another nightmare, seeing once more the victim going over the falls.

While the women picked him up in their boat we continued to struggle against the rapid. We paddled right into the centre again to where long weeds wavered out from the rocks. Two men jumped out and clutched the weeds. They held on with one hand and tied the painter to the weeds with the other. While the boat hung there we bailed it empty. The women came up in their canoes and took the *warishis* and drifted back to the bank. All of us except Amou and myself left the boat and swam ashore with a long rope and pulled us up as we kept it clear of rocks. Most of the men were bleeding from numerous cuts but pursued their task with single minds and great seriousness, and as the following days passed they toiled on tirelessly, with amazing stamina. Their harmonious team-work never broke down, and rarely did I hear personal criticism. Whoever made the right suggestion and showed a clear head was followed. After leaving the boats where we had found them we journeyed back to the village, taking two weeks from the falls; dead beat every night but fresh again next morning. They could have done the trip three times over. Their one thought was the forthcoming feast.

This fishing expedition had greatly cemented my relations with the Indians, for I had been one of them, not an employer or a visitor. I felt again the rightness of my place in the hills, the freedom and the zest of their life. I took no orders, gave none, and felt as uncomplicated and free as a bird. I looked on Labba and Amou as friends: Amou particularly, who, despite his thirty years, was as strong and swift-moving as a young buck, and as wise as the old men—an ancient youth wedded to the jungle.

CHAPTER FIVE

The Feast

FINALLY the journey ended. The paddles quickened, the canoes slid up to the landing-stage of the village; we heard the low note of a horn echoing from the mountains. The horn which they use is made simply by cleaning the inside and boring a small hole at the point of an eighteen-inch horn of a stray deer, whenever one is found in the frontier savannah. The outer end is strapped with hide and has a strong thong handle by which it is hung in one of the houses. It is blown every other day, sometimes more often, as the festive time approaches, directed according to the wind: if the air is still it is pointed to the mountains and the echo can be heard a long way off as a welcome to visitors. The Macoushi also use these horns but do not achieve the clear strong note that the Patamona make.

Amou explained this to me and called the horn *"pyala yapung."* *Yapung* means friend and *pyala* cow or bull: in this sense *yapung* is the general possessive indicating something "belonging" to the bull. This reveals the underlying idea of friendship for the Indian: possession. To the Indian life is like a web, in which the relationship of one thing to another is a binding cord. But this does not imply constriction: Indians are conscious of being bound to the mother jungle but are equally well aware of their freedom. In strange company their independence often appears as a depressing aloofness. However, the encroachment of civilisation has been bad for them: no longer are they entirely sure of the source of their spiritual being nor of the direction of their lives. Such things as an occasional sight by hunters, peering through the foliage, of a prospector driving in his boat with an outboard motor begin a succession of shocks that reverberate deeply in the Indian mind. These evidences of material power strike at the root of their little, careful skills with wood and creeper and at their partnership with the jungle. Like islanders, they are unused to contact and suffer badly when civilised man appears, however kind he may be, especially if he extols the excellence of his equipment. In admiring it they do not know the risks they run. They cannot see that such things may not be power, pure and simple, but compensations for something civilised man has lost; something which the Indians, despite the modesty of their understanding, still have.

As the boats came alongside, the villagers came running down the path. Their welcome was practical, for they started at once to relieve us of further work by unloading the fish, which were unpacked and strung up again for further drying by the women. To cover up my work of splitting the fish, they pressed the sides together and tied the fish to make them look whole again.

74

Once the work was under way they all began to chatter and laugh with relish at the thought of the fish. They began picking bits off here and there and soon everyone was munching. We were offered bowls of cassili; for me they had prepared a special brew of young cassava shoots, which ferments quickly and is usually reserved for the elders. After a moment or two I went to see my hut and made a thorough check. Nothing had been touched. Here and there the laths of the walls had been scraped by curious children attempting to look inside, but none had entered.

No one rested that day. The bowls were filled with cassili. The hunters came in with more meat and went out again. They had been busy and the village was well stocked. The women worked at the bakehouse, and as I lay in my hammock I had them in full view. Some baked the large pan-loaves of cassava bread, such as I had first seen in the Macoushi village; others prepared vast quantities of *cassili* liquor. The *mata-pees* hung about heavy with cassava and the children sat on their sticks to draw the juice. As the bowls filled, the women emptied them into the great pot, which had been cleaned with boiling water. When it was half full they added the leaves of the sac plant.

This herb gives the cassili a rich red colour as the liquid boils, the shade of red depending on when the sac is picked: early in its season it is brown. As the pot boiled, two girls, their eyes partly shut to avoid the steam, stood over it and stirred, occasionally adding water. They laughed and talked, working at the pot for over an hour. Then a small boy was sent off to fetch two more girls, who were, I had overheard, to be married to youths from another village at the coming feast. The new girls sat on either side of the pot, and Labba's mother and an old widow brought them two bowls of cassava husk, which they took without comment. As the other girls stirred, they chewed bits of the husk for five or six minutes until it formed a paste. This they shot on to their hands and rolled into balls, which they flicked into the pots. This continued until the bowls were emptied. The fire was partially

75

removed and the pot allowed to simmer, while all four women
—the crones joined in—began chewing cassava husk. But now
that the virgins had initiated the process, the others chewed
much longer until the cassava was a slimy liquid. This they also
shot into the pot. My stomach began to turn at the thought
of the *cassili* I had drunk during the past months without
my knowing exactly how it had been made.

I tipped myself out of my hammock and then saw Labba
ambling across, so I whistled to him and he started walking
towards me. The women realised that I had been watching
them and three of them ran away from the pot, leaving Labba's
mother, and began to laugh. They disappeared into the houses,
whispering to the others and giggling at me.

"Dirty," I said to Labba, "not good."

He laughed. "Good. Girls clean."

"How the girls clean?"

"Not married yet," he said.

"The older girls throwing too."

"Yes, they throw too. They clean because they only married
one year."

"Then why throw at all?" I asked.

"No eat and throw cassava, cassili no good. No grow
strong."

He told me that they had learnt that sugar would also
ferment the cassili but that they rarely got hold of any. This
explained the need for saliva. I realised that throughout the
feast I would be condemned to drink this cassili, so I suggested
that they make some extra bowls fermented with my sugar
for me. His grin faded and he stared at his toes: this meant
extra work. I said, with inspiration, that in exchange I would
show them how to make cassili without cassava at all. Labba
looked up and brightened: anything new was attractive, especially if it kept them in suspense until the final outcome. Labba
was too great a respecter of secretiveness to ask how I would
work the miracle. At once the girls got busy making my special
cassili ration.

The spirit of the festival grew. Men went to the savannah

to choose their headdresses from palm leaves; the women strung beads in the camp. The men picked old palms which they cut to the centre to remove the young yellow leaves: when slit, the budding fronds sprang out and each man took eight or nine palm centres and brought them back to lay in front of the huts. Besides headdresses, they cut skirts to hang nearly to their ankles. The headpiece was formed into a cone, as wide as the shoulders at the base, which completely covered the head, the summit rising in waving fronds. Around the upper arms other fronds would be tied. By making themselves look like walking plants the men identified themselves with the jungle. In this the Patamona are different from other tribes I have seen, who decorate themselves only with bright feathers. The Patamona use their feathers strung in a chain which swings down their backs from the nape of the neck, and the wings and heads of blue, yellow and red toucans, powice and other birds stand out at intervals from the long tail-feathers hanging to their waists. Green waving heads, bronze torsos and fluttering plumes would be the motif of the dance.

Then the men cut poles seven feet long as dancing staves and shaved them clean with stones. They cut into the ends so that when struck on the ground the staves whirred like a snare drum. The women made different coloured ribbons to tie round their foreheads and necks, with bead strings to cover their breasts to the waist. They went to the river and washed their bead aprons, their ankle, leg, arm and wrist bands. Some of them had made dresses from the cloth I had given them—they like making dresses, and clothing appears to reduce the number of colds and chills they suffer, which seems to be the main cause of their fatal or serious illnesses —but most of them were worn out, so they fell back on their normal clothes. They collected plants and berries from which they made dyes: coral for their lips and dark blue for eyebrows, which normally they shave off. Some of the older women, past the early years of marriage, had these facial decorations permanently tattooed on them, with three wavy blue lines on their foreheads as the tribal mark. In this way

77

all the decorations and costumes were collected, but none was tried on: they knew they would fit and would not anticipate their enjoyment. Now they thought of their guests.

Cassili was decanted into many large gourds; meat was taken from the rafters and cut; the *warishis* were loaded and parties set off along various trails to set up food stores at stages towards the village. The meat was wrapped in leaves, tied and suspended from a branch at each place to prevent animals from reaching it; the cassili stoppered in the gourds and placed at the foot of the tree, with a small vent left to allow the fermentation gases to escape. The most distant cache was only five miles away, but this is a considerable distance in the jungle.

It had taken the villagers about ten days to make all these preparations since the return of the fishing party, and it was now the first week in December. They said they waited for the full moon of the festival, which I thought would make it about New Year's Day, although without an almanac I could not be sure. I had tried to keep a diary by cutting notches on a stick outside my hut, but discovered later that it had been inaccurate, as I had missed three or four days.

After this a lazy spell came over the village, as it usually does between bursts of work, and they all lay swinging in their hammocks. Then they cleaned up the houses—a rare thing—pulled up stumps and swept away stones from the dance circle in the village centre. They cut a path straight from the village to the creek, uprooting cassava and anything else that lay in the line, keeping it smoothed and swept clean like the rest. As I stood watching them working, Labba's mother came over from the village.

"*Amako inipei*—the old man is sick."

I said I thought he was probably tired after all the work.

"No, no," she said, wagging her head and laughing. "Play lazy no good."

I went to the old man's house and found him lying in his hammock. When I asked him what was wrong he said nothing, but rubbed his stomach. I suggested that perhaps he had drunk too much cassili, the fresh kind, and been slightly poisoned,

78

for although it is rare for an Indian to take cassili from which the prussic acid of the cassava has not been properly strained, it seemed to be a possibility. But as I had no means of knowing, I gave him two or three phensic tablets as a general faith cure. He was up that evening talking with the others. His wife said the tablets had given him new vigour and suggested I give some to everyone in the village.

"Feast come. Dance plenty," she said. "Indian punish plenty."

I saw that the villagers hoped the pills would prevent tiredness in front of the guests and enable them to put on an amazing performance. Endurance is the pride of an Indian dancer as much as the steps he makes, for the dance usually lasts three days and two nights without a single break. I laughed away her impossible demands and went back to my hut.

During the next few nights they became more serious and took life gravely, as though conscious of some spiritual overtone to the season they prepared for. I, too, felt contemplative and sat often in the evenings reading. They came round and sat about in the yellow pool cast by my lamp, as if seeking conversation or some wise saw or observation that would strike a chord and set them at ease. Labba and Amou, the boldest ones, came and sat beside me and asked what kind of paper I had, meaning my book. I turned to Amou and explained that it was a Bible, a book about God. To my surprise all those around looked at each other and sighed "Ooouu." I felt slightly embarrassed and tried to read, as I had no wish to be turned into a missionary, but they crept closer and Labba's mother, having been informed, came running from her house, squatted in front of me and held out her hand.

"You tell me. You tell me," she said.

So I did my best with passages chosen here and there to tell them simply of Christianity's first events. They remained quite silent throughout my halting words until I went back to explain Christmas. They asked what kind of place a manger would be found in and I said it would be like their village.

79

Naturally enough they were surprised. "No," one said, standing up. "He come big place. Nice place."

They refused to consider the birth of God anywhere that was not fine, and I found that unless I frequently mentioned the word God they were bored. But we talked for more than three hours, and at the end I noticed that the old man, who had been standing, was pale. I was afraid he had a temperature and suggested he sit, but he refused, saying he would stand and that I must say plenty more. So I went on, noticing the old man look at his wife and call her away. They went back to their house, and I stopped and looked at the rest. We heard the squeak of the hammock ropes as the old people lay down. Rarely had the villagers been so still, and I could hear the waters between the stones in the creek and the breeze rustling the cassava trees. I said I would talk to them some other time, and they slipped away, murmuring in their houses about my having a book and that perhaps I could show them how to get in touch with God. I sat waiting for something to happen and eventually the old woman came back. She walked over to me with a smile to reassure me.

"*Pi-eye* man not come yet—the wise man has not come. Old man very ill," she said.

I knew they had sent to another village for a wise man who could deal with the spirits which control sickness. Now she asked if I would give "God medicine" instead.

I went the next morning and spent several long nights by him in the next week. They did not realise how ill he was, interested only in what I said about religion and attending to my wants as never before. I came to the conclusion that the old man had a serious attack of dysentery: his temperature remained high, and I felt that his case was beyond me, but I did my best for him. I started him on sulphathiazole and peppermint oil and spent hours worrying over his treatment. There was no help to be sought and I felt the weight of the responsibility, especially as I was attached to him and saw that the rest of them now had a touching and quite unwarranted faith in me.

His wife saw how ill he was by his rapid loss of weight and she began to feed him by her hand. When she was busy instructing the young girls in the rites of the feast, the other old woman, the widow, who was a distant relative, looked after him. To the surprise of the women the old man rose one morning and walked out in a dazed state. I jumped from my hammock and watched him from my hut door. He walked to the highest and clearest knoll near the village and looked at the quarters of the sky, listening and taking deep, refreshing breaths. Then he began to shake with an ague. I ran to hold him. He looked at me and his lips trembled as if to speak.

"Come, let's go back to the house."

He shook his head firmly. "*Canai, canai*—no, no."

He held my hand pressing it hard. Knowing them by now, I realised he wanted my friendship but no talk. I tried to lead him off the knoll but he would not move. He looked at the sky again.

"*Yapung, akay toneh yabu*—The big rains will come."

"No, the sun is out, shining bright. Plenty Indians come."

"I know," he said, "Indians on trail now near here."

Then he repeatedly told me that the big rains would come in two moons' time and flood the rivers. I told him, yes, we all knew that, for rains normally come in March.

"When big floods come I go with them."

"You cannot go anywhere. You are too ill."

"*Yapung*, me go. Me go far."

I realised that he was predicting his death and had chosen to tell me. I took him back to his hammock and returned to my hut, depressed. The children took no interest and the older ones merely looked in now and then in passing if they heard him groan. I tried to brighten myself and the village and took my harmonica one morning to the houses. I sat by the huge cassili canoes and played in the old man's house. They crowded round smiling and everyone's spirits rose. A little thing like this can have a great effect on a small community isolated in the jungle, and for the first time in eleven days the old man smiled. The slower pieces did not interest them, but when I played

81

the more rhythmic Latin American tunes their toes flicked in time. Later I discovered that one or two of them were close to the beat of their dance. After a long session they brought me some of my special cassili, placing the bowl at my feet, as usual, for Indians rarely give food or drink into one's hand, as they normally eat in a squatting position. They drank also, occasionally stirring the liquor with pieces of carved stick which they kept as stirrers, tucked in their *saloes* or on a stool. That night the old man had a good rest.

Next morning all were up early and I found them standing motionless in a knot on the hill, expectantly looking in the direction of the higher waters of the creek. I asked a girl what was wrong. She whispered:

"Indians coming."

"Now?"

"Now."

Indians were certainly in the district, as the old man had said, for a gun report had been heard early that morning. But I could see or hear no other sign of them. The girl said the visitors were now feasting on the food left out to entice them on. The moon would be full in two nights. The villagers left the hill and began last-minute preparations, every now and then whispering to me almost as if they were afraid, "Indians coming." They seemed unhappy for prospective hosts, but their anxiety is partly shyness, which they feel even for those of their own kind, springing from the isolation in which each village chooses to live, and partly the genuine dread that most people feel when putting on a formal reception. But there was also real fear on some faces.

"Why you all look so angry when others coming for feast?" I asked.

"Sometime other Indians come, not this tribe, and eat plenty, drink plenty and carry another man wife." During this time affairs between visiting men and the local women are not uncommon, and the younger ones may be enticed away with fine gifts. Of course, when the turn of this village came round to go visiting, about once every three years, its men were not above the same practices, although they were generally regarded as immoral. I assured them at once that I would see to it that no Indians left the village, which they were pleased to hear. I had made another rash promise. Then Amou, with his usual brightness, asked about the special liquor I had promised.

"You make drink," he said. "Me see, me see."

"Oh," I said vaguely, "we make now."

I thought desperately and called to the girls to hurry to get two gourds and wash them out. They ran down to the creek and returned in a minute. I had sugar, lots of fresh rainwater, some syrup of lime. Lemonade? Then I remembered that the Brazilians had a drink of great potency if kept long—simply yeast, water and sugar. I had plenty of yeast. (I had not thought of yeast before, otherwise I should have made my cassili ferment with it.) I got the gourds, filled them with water and mixed in plenty of yeast and sugar. I had two days for the brew to mature, and as I stoppered the gourds they watched attentively. The gourds I left buried in the moist sand where they would keep cool.

On the last day all the hammocks were brought out of the houses and slung round the dance space in a circle, with a small shelter of palm leaves built over each. That night Amou took it upon himself to be a co-leader of the dance with Labba. Everyone sat around a large fire and when I came they asked me to sit comfortably near it. I could think of nothing to talk about. As usual, my bowl of cassili arrived, but for almost half an hour everyone remained silent. I noticed that Amou had placed himself at a little distance from us. He bent his head in his arm and pushed his feet out in front of him although the soles were still flat on the ground; after a while he began very softly tapping his broad foot. Indians have a great capacity for sensing an atmosphere, for getting in the mood, and this long silence had tempered their minds acutely. They all knew that he was not tapping idly. He was starting to weave the spell of the feast. So, in fact, it begins from the smallest beginning; a foot tapped to slow time in the sand.

83

He tapped on, gradually more deliberately, and began to talk of the old man who lay near him in his hammock. He is sick now, said Amou in a low voice, still with his head in his arm, but he will be well again. He must not be afraid. He had good medicine from Yapung—that was their name for me—and he must believe that God is good, very good and beautiful. He emphasised these two qualities, for to the Patamona goodness and beauty are inseparable: two sides of the same quality. Also, continued Amou, "our God is Indian God." He stressed this as he had done many days before when the subject was first mentioned. Amou was proud of his blood. He tapped on for some minutes, stopped suddenly, and then started tapping with both feet and humming short notes of medium pitch. This was the beginning of the melody which runs through the whole feast. As he hummed he brought in one or two words indistinctly and stopped, repeating the humming and words again after a pause.

Eventually he stopped altogether and there was silence. He had tried on their behalf to see if the spell of the feast was alive but none had joined in his singing. The mood was not yet full and ripe. I sat there for some time and then felt the old man's forehead: he was nearly normal. I brought some phensic and hoped that he could keep his temperature down before the feast. By this time his wife sat by him constantly, keeping a fire burning near his head. I brought a blanket and tied it into his hammock, for it it had been loose someone would have taken it without thinking of depriving the old man, and his wife would probably have laughed. They have no idea of elementary precautions against chills, although they value medicine in pills and bottles.

Next morning they were up before sunrise. The cassili canoes were dragged out, put on stands and filled, and gourds filled with drinks were put by each hammock and the dance space weeded and swept once more. They were in a purposeful mood and I found it unwise to ask questions or suggest anything. From the creek I heard the knocks of paddles on *curee-ole* sides, sounding in consecutive beats to indicate how

84

many canoes were coming. Three boats came in sight, filled from stem to stern. I counted about forty Indians, about twice as many as lived in the village, including children and old men. The villagers collected together, whispering and looking uncertain once more. Amou, Labba, and a man called John, who had been on the frontier, from where he had taken his name, came out and put on their costumes; the waving green hats, brilliant feather-tails and skirts. They took their staves and conferred seriously in low tones like so many heraldic beasts. John went down the path alone from the dance space to tell the women and children they could approach and were welcome. The other two adjusted the sticks of impaled dried fish with which they would begin the greeting.

As the women and children arrived, Amou and Labba belaboured them with the fish. In a moment every one was laughing and screaming, jostling and snatching pieces of fish. Amou and Labba cried as they struck, *"Sileh! Sileh! Sileh!—* It's eating time!"* The women sidled out of the scrimmage and began talking to the wives of the village, some of the younger ones staying in the melee with the fish, crouching and yelling. A baby started bawling, but no one took any notice. Amou and Labba then formed up side by side facing John. By this time the men were coming from the creek in file, every ten paces or so giving out a loud high Indian yell: "Yih-eeee!" The older men led, and the foremost was in the palm dress. The others were in *saloes*, or had shirts or short pants traded at the frontier and worn as their best suits. Two had ancient felt hats and another a Brazilian straw with no crown. Some had bows, others guns and the rest long staves. Now they stamped in rhythm, shuffling two steps, stopping and banging their sticks on the ground so that their ends thrummed, and yelling again. The shuffling speeded up until the shrrr-shrrr of the sticks was a constant beat. They began to march, lifting their feet six inches off the ground and waving their heads from side to side.

Amou and Labba stepped forward, raised their staves and began calling out in Patamona very rapidly, greeting the "visitors from far away" and wishing them to stay long. They turned about with John and began stamping off with their staves. Amou dropped out for a moment and stood by the old man's house, lifting his hand and chanting again, this time to tell the visitors that there was a sick one among them, mentioning God several times, using the English word. Then without checking his voice he began humming the melody of the feast while the others were silent. He raised his eyes to the sky and began singing and banging the rhythm with his feet, until he moved into the circle and the others formed behind him in twos, linking arms, sometimes men together, sometimes a youth and a girl.

They followed him, taking three steps sideways, three backwards, then to the other side and repeat. Amou began to weave more complicated steps, stamping, swaying and swinging round gracefully. The others followed. All of them joined his voice and sang in chorus.

> "*Waki kuli! Kapung yabu-uuuu.*
> *Indekou tukay casiliiiiii*
> *Tukay akiiii casiliiiiiii . . .*"

dragging out the last notes.

Then the following chorus, the first line a high-pitched humming, the second line starting high then descending to a low and solemn tone:

> "*Heigh-yay-yay-yay-yay, yay-yay-yay,*
> *Hila-hinn;*
> *Hila-hinn.*"

"How good that all Indians come here—drink plenty—eat plenty—have a very good time!"

The chorus in English roughly translates:

> "Hooray. Hooray!
>   [meaning also, "This is the rhythm"]
> We have come to pray;
> We have come to pray."

86

This was then repeated with impromptu yells thrown in. A drummer in the corner took up the beat and the men began to whistle through small bamboo pipes. As they blew, they bowed as if to someone. With the drum, the whirr of the staves, the women keeping the chorus going and the whistling, they produced a joyful, weird and yet fascinating sound.

As individuals dropped out sweating for a rest, girls came forward with bowls of cassili. The dancer parted his palm fronds, swilled wildly and linked arms to circulate once more, with cassili dribbling down his stomach.

As the hours wore on to early morning more dropped out, the drinking and revelry increased, but still the file continued jogging, singing, and whistling round the ring. John came forward as leader for a change. By this time he was drunk, his hair plastered over his face and his voice hoarse and thick: he was thoroughly happy. He began stamping vigorously and yelling, the others following him in a hectic shuffling and bounding. His eyes rolled and were glazed. He drew far ahead of the others and his feet beat a fast tattoo beyond the drum beat; then he stood in one place, stamping and jerking his arms about as if galvanised. As he worked himself up the others yelled. Sweat streamed; the flames leapt. His hair fell about like seaweed. Instead of singing he groaned and gasped and his stomach heaved. He clasped his hands and quivered, shaking from head to feet like a bow-string, became rigid for seconds and fell like a stone, puffing the dust around him.

Two men rolled him aside and the drum picked up. The dance swept on with greater zest. The village apparently had shown its vitality. I ran to John. Someone remarked thickly that I should bring him to, so I emptied a gourd over his head and he staggered to his feet. When he focused on me, a grin slid crookedly across his gleaming face.

"Yapung. Me drink. Me happy!"

I walked off to my hut and John reeled after me. I sat in the doorway and he squatted down, gabbling happily. I gave him a cigarette of Brazilian tobacco. He got up and wandered

87

in the direction of the creek; I heard a crash in the cassava and imagined him squatting somewhere being sick: Brazilian tobacco is strong. I lay down to snatch some sleep but heard the visiting Indians creeping around and decided that as they were strange people I had better keep awake. I sat by my lamp turning over a year-old magazine, and an ancient man, a Patamona, walked up uninvited. I turned slowly and he stopped, then grinned toothlessly.

"You should not walk upon people like that."

He grinned with amiable stupidity and squatted by me, beckoning the others to come in. They crowded in, squatted and gazed about them, interested even in my shoes.

"*Cassili icheh?*—You want cassili?" I asked, wondering how I could get rid of them. I went out and collected my gourds of fire-water. When I opened the cork, fumes wafted up. I looked at the old man and reflected that he would do very well as the first guinea pig. He tipped up the gourd and gurgled, put it down and placed the palms of his hands on the floor.

"You make?"

"Yes."

"Good," he belched. "Very good."

Again the moronic grin. "What you make it with?"

"Poison," I said simply.

His lips shrivelled and he sagged. Slowly a titter trickled around him, then belly laughs. The old man inflated himself once more and bared his gums, wagging his head. He drank the rest and asked for more. Eight or nine of the others between them finished the first gourd and went out with the good news among the dancers. Three hours later, as dawn broke, I walked to the feast and recognised some of my guests prostrated in the sand, rolling about with mirth. Others began asking for my firewater. I refused the visitors, as clearly they had had enough to be going on with, but I shook up the rest of the liquor and emptied it into the cassili boats. They rushed for the special blend, scooping it up and drinking as fast as they

88

could, shaking their heads, grunting and nudging each other. The general opinion was that it tasted much better than the local brew, although I was sure the dilution in the cassili prevented them from more than tasting it.

By this time the party was shaking down. Couples lay in the sand; others slumped against convenient trees. A few dancers kept moving and the drum still banged. Everywhere feathers, palm fronds, whistles and beads lay scattered in the churned sand. I knew that out of sight in the cassava couples were more actively engaged. Some of those with the skill to match their lasciviousness had stayed sober to pursue the women more effectively. I learnt that if a husband caught a stranger with his wife on such an occasion he would do no more than scowl: a coolness would exist between them thereafter, but nothing more. The older men went for the wives and the young men for the girls. The parents tried to keep track of their daughters: if they were missing from the ring the mothers looked for them, frequently asking me first. I usually said they were all with me and they were reassured: I saw no point in being mixed up in such domestic tangles. In any case the parents had been young once and the present generation was probably no worse. The chief impediment to romance seemed to be the children, for whenever a couple whispered and wandered off the children would follow them and much ingenuity was spent escaping them.

The first night naturally led to the marriage ceremonies of the second evening. A certain amount of selection and pretasting had already taken place, and the girls knew who would propose to them. Three girls from the visitors and the two from the village who had made the cassili were to marry.

Meanwhile the dancing kept going and I noticed that the elderly man who had led the visitors from the creek was still on his feet. He had been going, I estimated, for twenty hours. Labba took the lead in the morning and by midday was approaching the usual frenzy. After leaping, yelling and shaking he collapsed like John. They rolled him aside and went on.

Amou, pale, shaky, and smiling fixedly, kept on. When I looked at him he would laugh and throw his hair back calling me to drink. This was now their only thought.

I looked at the old man and he was much the same as he had been. I was annoyed to see that they persistently gave him cassili. I tried to stop them but it was useless, despite the fact that his wife sat by him. I picked up a roasted boar's leg and sat chewing.

"You go and dance," I said to the old woman. "I will look after the old man."

"She is too old to dance," he laughed.

"Go on," I said, lifting her arm. She giggled.

"You come and dance with me," she said.

I apologised, explaining that this was their party: I could not dance in such an affair. Eventually she walked into the ring with one of the girls and started to sing in a quavering voice, to which no one paid attention. Despite their revelry, it was not done to be amused at another's shortcomings in the rites of the reason. The old woman danced for an hour and then returned, but I sat on and talked with the old man. He did not say much and appeared to be in great pain. I asked him if he would like me to help him to walk a few steps outside the camp and the noise. He pointed to his legs and said that he could not move them; I felt them and they were cold. The sickness was now obviously serious. I collected some strips of lint and heated them in a little pot over his fire and put poultices on his feet. When I asked him if there was an improvement he said he could not feel.

I left him and called his wife to my hut. She padded along beside me glancing frequently at me. When she was seated I told her that the old man was now very sick. She agreed but said he would get better sometime. I said it was worse than she thought: he would go very soon. Something in her mind insulated it against the possibility and she would not grasp the warning. Eventually, after I had pointed out his symptoms in detail, his cold legs, his swollen feet, she left and went to his hammock. Affectionately she stroked his head and closed his eyes, soothing him and running the other hand down to feel his swollen feet. She came out of the firelight with me and walked away holding my hand, talking brokenly and then crying a little: saying the old man would leave her alone. I reassured her: she would be looked after and I would give him more treatment the next morning. There seemed to be nothing else to say.

Meanwhile the hammocks of the marriageable girls had been slung round the ring and the girls stood by them for some time to make sure that the youths knew which were theirs. As the ring danced round, one youth slipped out unnoticed, put his hand across the hammock as if he were tired and needed a rest. He looked about surreptitiously to make sure no one saw him, lay back apparently in an offhand way, and rolled in. The girls had left and were mingling with the dancers. So, one by one, the youths made their choice, sealed the marriage and lay swinging in the hammocks. Later the boy's parents would visit the village and bring gifts if they could afford anything. I walked over to John, one of the newly-weds, who was standing near the hammock of his bride. I congratulated him and said I hoped he would be a good hunter.

"I will if you give me a gun," he replied with surprising smartness. Clearly the influence of the frontier had sharpened his acquisitive wits.

I talked with the two girls from our village and they gave me some cassili. I lifted it and drank, then reached back for support. Absentmindedly I leant on a hammock that I had not noticed in the shadow. Labba stood up and came over in mock agitation.

"Yapung, you no want this one. Not this one."

I withdrew hastily and walked to my camp, Labba following, splashing his cassili gourd.

"Who is it?"

"Old one. Come, me show you."

Sure enough it was a crone, who must have been a grandmother. She had put up her sign in the hope of luck, and I had nearly been caught. The marriage arrangement is, apart from any significance of the hammock, a cunning device to trap men tired from the dancing and drinking.

After the marriages, the dancing cooled off perceptibly. Next morning our village summoned the dregs of its energy so as to give a final display of its rôle as the energetic host. I poured a few pounds of beads out of my store into a bowl and called the women of the other village to my hut and distributed them. Apart from the occasion, it was an investment, for Indians never forget a kindness received, and I did not know when I might not depend on their help at some future time. The end of the party approached with less ceremony than the start. The visitors shook hands all round—the one quick clasp that is only given by Indians at parting, accompanied by averted eyes. The women were the last to part, talking animatedly to each other about children, new aprons and other domestic matters.

Once in the boats, the guests were given a rousing sendoff, shouts and yells contrasting with the stiff reception of three days before. Jokes and compliments were flung to and fro. They paddled slowly out of sight and the villagers turned back upon the hill. Four dancers still shuffled round the ring, including the youths married into the village. The drummer looked up, stopped banging, and rose and kicked the drum, so that it rolled across the ring. The dancers dropped their arms and walked off. Silence. It was the end of the season. So it closed with as little concern as it had started.

In the years ahead there were other feasts, but the first will always be the best memory. It was festivity in the unspoilt mountain Indian spirit. But one other I recall for the prelude of fishing among the sands of Waratak below the great falls, after the usual journey by canoe. It was a morning after we had set the lines when all of us—I was now a seasoned hunter—set out on our own. Some of the men were skimming up and down the river in their woodskins checking the lines and collecting the fish. I had crossed the river in my own woodskin and was prowling around with my gun.

I passed an abandoned farm, probably made by a prospector, past thick brambles, now crackling in the dry heat, and through a sea of parched fern, crossed a series of hillocks and small inlets from the main stream, and came towards some lines we had set a few hundred yards from the falls. The wind shifted and the noise of the falls came booming down the canyon. My gun was slung from my shoulder by the strap, but I held its weight to swing it down quickly on sight of game, for in that season it is not uncommon to catch deer or other large animals in search of lusher vegetation swimming the river and providing good targets. Ahead was a great sandhill carved to a sharp bluff where the river had scoured in spate, and I made for it over an intervening patch of fallen trees and sand spits through which the water surged gently from the wind moving the river beyond. I swung over logs, holding old branches and jumping from one dry patch to the next. Among the rotting trunks lay, here and there, sparkling clear water, running to and fro over the sand, and I pushed down into one of these gullies for a drink.

I hung my gun on a branch and stooped in the thicket to the sand and cut away some of the brambles. When I had drunk I sat on the sand to light a cigarette, but I had no matches. I looked about for a dry branch or a flint but there was nothing with which to make a fire, so I replaced the cigarette in my shirt pocket and fastened the buttons. I removed my canvas shoes and knotted the laces to sling them from my shoulder, intending to paddle through the cool water and the sand. I reached up for my gun with my left hand without looking and stood up to jump upon the logs to the next creek. As I swung my hand quickly forward to reach a branch I felt a sudden bruising pain behind my right shoulder as if punched by a blunt stick and a jab as of a needle. I held the branch with my hand but slipped, the gun sliding through my hand to strike the sand, and I involuntarily turned round on my grip. I felt a rush of cold sweat at the thought of the gun firing and stepped back in the same instant to recover my balance. The labaria snake was twined in the brambles at my right, coming in view as I swung back, its head moving from side to side and looking ahead of me, where my shoulder had been a split second before.

At the same moment my gun came sliding towards me along the log and I grabbed it, sweeping it round on him and firing with my left hand. The labaria dropped to the sand uninjured and began weaving away on the sand with a sideways movement. I tried to work the breech action on my repeater with my right hand but it would not obey, already half paralysed. I sat down suddenly and began to tremble and sweat with uncontrollable fear. I fumbled with my left hand, hanging the gun in the crook of my right arm and worked the breech, ripping the palm of my hand in my clumsiness. The snake was still moving, now about fifteen feet away, and I made another left-hand shot. He slid hastily between some rotten logs and vanished.

I ripped my shirt with my left hand and squeezed the flesh of my shoulder over till I could see two small blue punctures where the fangs had sunk. I squeezed around the marks, being careful not to bring pressure directly on them for fear of breaking the poison shells shed by the fangs, which I thought were still in the punctures. I began to feel sick and started dragging myself through the sand and mud under the brambles towards the river and reached the water's edge, my will and power of thought continuing to disintegrate in flashes of nightmarish visions mixed with a kaleidoscope of the bright sun, the mud and the impersonal sparkling river. It was less than three minutes, perhaps, since the strike. I sat for a moment without being able to make a proper decision, trying to yell but only producing a croak. I had not the sense to fire my gun and I could not reach the bite with my knife to cut it. I began to slide towards the water as if it were a route of escape, and only at the last minute I realised that I was committing myself to drowning in the fast stream or death from the electric eels swarming in those waters, and hauled myself back. By now I was feeling waves of nausea and weakness, my brain, apparently disintegrating rapidly, full of conflicting messages, fantasies and commands. Some higher consciousness still strove alone above the mounting tide of chaos and I moved my gun in a series of jerks to my lap. I looked across the river but could see no Indians and felt drowsy.

A decision to fire the gun eventually struggled through and

I began slowly and deliberately to fill the magazine with my left hand. For a moment my head cleared, and then I felt a freezing in my guts and a warmness between my thighs: I knew my lower muscles were losing control and that I was unable to retain my water. I felt another wave of horror and cramped up my legs, which still worked, and loaded feverishly. Putting the gun between my knees and pointing it at the water I began to fire as rapidly as possible the three rounds in the magazine. Again I managed to reload and fire another two shots. I felt sleepy but I had no more pain except when I tried to move my useless right arm. I squeezed around the punctures for a moment then lolled back on the mud, dropping my gun, and I gazed stupefied at the dancing water, wanting desperately to be on smooth sand open to the sky where I could die cleanly away from the filth I lay in.

Suddenly I realised that ten minutes must have elapsed since the strike and that the bite could not be fatal, although I knew that I could not live without attention soon. Then I heard a rapid tattoo of a paddle and a long whistle. I glimpsed Peta some yards away darting glances under the bushes. He saw me and stopped his woodskin.

"Achineh, achineh—quick," I said as loudly as I could.

He jumped out of his woodskin and it sank. Standing in the water he cupped his hands and gave a long call; at once an answer echoed back and two curee-oles shot from the opposite bank, coursing over the surface at great speed. Peta splashed up to me, looked around wild-eyed and then tore off his saloe, winding it round my shoulder above the bite and screwing the knot to make a tourniquet. His rigid Indian modesty was sacrificed by this but he had nothing else at hand. By the time he had made the knot tight the others had arrived. Only then I remembered that I had a snake-stone and a medicine called Brazilian Especifico, and took a long draught. They lifted the logs and cut the bushes behind me, making a clear path along which I was gently carried to the clear sand. Labba arrived and soon had a fire going, sending a boy for some herbs which he boiled. He removed the stone and handed the mushed leaves to one of the girls who squeezed them into the cut. Almost at once I felt a deep burning. They began to massage my arms and the girl heated another type of leaf, putting it over the bite and binding it. Labba heated a third brew and made me drink it. By now I was feeling much relieved although exhausted and I had a rapidly rising temperature.

Labba said I must not be moved and they cut branches and leaves, making a shelter over me where I lay. They brought my hammock over the river and eased me into it. For three days I lay quietly until I could get up for short intervals, with my right arm in my shirt. After a week I could walk and then recovered for the journey home. But for some months afterward whenever I drank much I felt a great itching where I had been bitten, and the bites rose up in two small cones. Fortunately the poison shells had not been left in the wound. The bite could not have been perfectly made, or perhaps the snake had struck at something else a short time before attacking me, otherwise the poison would have worked before they could have reached me. It was the only time that I was bitten in five years and it happened because of my own carelessness in going through the brushwood so hastily. After that time I began to develop the Indian capacity to smell snakes and was rarely surprised again. I have never heard of an Indian being bitten: they can usually tell a snake is about a good distance before they reach it and never disturb them or kill them unless necessary.

CHAPTER SIX

Prospect of Diamonds

AFTER the feast I went often to my farm. The path was well worn by now, twisting and turning up and down hillocks through the jungle for about four miles; the stones were pressed down and the Indians' broad feet had left a shiny snake-like trail. Many of the trees on either side had been slashed by passing villagers going to and fro to weed, which they did voluntarily after the feast. As I came towards the farm I welcomed the sheet of light that began to pour through the greenness, let in by the clearing, a beckoning brightness that grew at each

97

step. It was my other home, peaceful and spacious, although it was a mere four acres hemmed by tall trees.

I used to go to a large half-burnt log in the centre of the patch, from where I looked about me at the slope of crops. The corn was about knee-high, the plantain suckers were well out, the cassava was sprouting and the black-eyed beans, which I had brought to eat and then sown, were ready for picking. Their leaves, I discovered, made good green vegetables. The bananas and peppers still had some way to go. All must be ripe before the big rains in May. The farm had been going for only four months and I was pleased.

As the birds sang and the bats squeaked in the dead trees hollowed by rot, I thought of all my plans for the future. When the sun came and made an oven of the clearing I made a small shade from the palm leaves over my seat. By this time I must have looked like a Robinson Crusoe stranded on a mountain after a receding flood. My khaki trousers had long ago rotted from below the knees from frequent drenchings, and I had cut them short and patched my canvas shoes with the cloth. By now I frequently went barefoot, although it was nearly a year before my feet could take the jagged ironstone hills.

The Indians still regarded me as an unfailing source of supply, particularly of powder and shot. Often I heard the hunters far from the village blazing away needlessly, which was doubly annoying, as my supplies were by now dangerously low. I was in a dilemma. I needed supplies to continue prospecting; I must find diamonds to pay for the supplies. The imminent rains made an early visit to the frontier urgent, but there was the old man, whom I could not yet leave. It was now January and the first rains came in March; the heavier ones later in May. Before the rains I not only had to strike diamonds but make the long trek to the frontier and back. There was much hurried work ahead. If there had been a partner I could have been three times richer and more certain of my life. Of these problems and anxieties I told the Indians nothing, lest it upset our good relations.

The old man was slowly sinking. By now even the Indians felt the constraint of his illness. The young hunters would, by custom, mention to him that they were going out: as he was often asleep his wife would answer for him and point out, with her head sunk wearily on her arm, that they should respect his state and not gallivant about the jungle. So they sat about idly, still expecting him to recover. The respect in which the old man was held was considerable. He was the oldest in the village. He had shown all the men the tricks of hunting, the trails and the customs of their race. He was the counsel in time of trouble and still the best weather oracle among them.

Frequently the old woman would become alarmed at her husband's state and call me to see him quickly. I would go and feel his pulse and reassure her. Then I would walk off to a distance and watch her through the door. Every now and then while he slept she would take a leaf and hold it over his mouth to see if his breath moved it. It was when it remained still, possibly because of the angle in which she held it, that she ran to me.

The old man had lost half his weight by this time and was a skeleton of hollows, sinews and folded skin, although his legs kept the muscular Indian form. I was sure that half his trouble arose from the Indian habit of giving him cold cassili every morning, but it was a habit I could not break. I gave him hot herb teas and ginger tea to bring down the fever, phensic tablets and crushed sulpha tablets, three times a day for three weeks. Probably this was too small a dose spread over too long a time, but I had no means of knowing. The ginger tea seemed particularly effective in reducing the fever in the evenings. The villagers sat around watching at each visit. I often wondered why they did not employ their own method of treatment, for although the *pi-eye* man had not come, there was a youth, one of those recently married into the village, who had been initiated into the *pi-eye* dance and spells.

One evening, after such a visit, I walked back to my hut and sat on the steps. The moon was very bright and I scratched in the sand with a stick, wondering what I would do when the old man died. I had never touched a corpse before and never seen a man buried; but now it seemed that having been mis-

99

sionary and doctor I was to be the undertaker; a grim procession of tasks from the spiritual to the grossly material. I put off the unpleasant prospect and turned in, fully dressed. As the moonbeams traced their steady course across the hut floor I lay and smoked and dreamed. Eventually I rose to turn off the lamp. As I glanced through the door I saw the village fires dying away. This was strange and I felt my skin tighten with some premonition.

The smoke dwindled, too, and I knew that only sand thrown on a fire could produce this effect. I heard leaves rustling as figures moved into the old man's house. I wondered if he were already dead and this the way they accepted death. A figure ran out of the hut, so I returned to my hammock from where I could watch without being suspected, as I was sure now that the doused fires meant that they were up to something they did not want me to observe. The cracking of small branches followed as someone broke off bushes in the jungle fringe. It struck me as dangerous to venture in the jungle at night. It was now after twelve and the children were fast asleep. No sound. I felt that the person had returned to the hut. Two hours passed. Then I heard one of the low benches being dragged in the sand. Leaves rustled and a soft moaning wavered out as if someone were in pain. It was not the old man, I was sure. The moan rose louder to a high-pitched wail and broke into a muffled song. Again the voice rose, to a feminine screech and the song came loudly; then it faded again, and so it rose and fell. When the breeze dropped momentarily I caught the words "evil" and "spirit" and it must be "driven from the sick." The last line went:

"When the sun is up this sickness will go."

Then the voice was lost in the swishing of leaves. Stamping began: it sounded like a single pair of feet. I reached the side of the house, where there were some bushes. Indians are expert at peeping. They will sit for perhaps fifteen minutes parting each single leaf and twig and placing it gently behind their necks, until eventually the face is framed in the bush so that

100

they can see clearly without a hint of their presence being given. Should an Indian have done this near to me I would have smelt him, but I was sure that I had not developed their strong body odour. So I confidently began to part the bushes in their way and finally found myself looking into the doorway of the hut.

The old man lay with his eyes open, his wife sitting beside him, her hands on her knees, staring into space. Outside the hut the moon gleamed on the twisting dancing body of the *pi-eye* youth as he thrashed the branches he held in his hand. The boy beat his branches faster, drew near the hammock and struck all about it. As he struck the door the breeze of the branches wafted over my face. I was only seven feet from him. I did not move and prayed that he would come no nearer. He stopped beating and stamping and stood stiffly with humped shoulders, retching as if to bring up some vile substance. Finally he stilled his bobbing head and swung the branches over it in a motion as of ejection. He gave a wild startling scream and fell to the ground, lying still for five minutes, until the moaning started again, this time an easy lullaby, a humming of the previous melody. In his half-ecstatic dance he seemed to be trying to symbolise the old man's struggles for life and to have taken them upon himself. The final gestures and the scream could have denoted the ejection of the sickness. Now he apparently lay in a state of quiet convalescence. He started singing softly the song he had sung before which, curiously, had the same melody, though with a slower tempo, as the festival song. I slowly replaced each leaf as I had parted it and slipped back to my hut, at each step brushing out the footprints behind me.

Next morning I was keen to see the state of the village, but walked down trying to appear unconcerned. The Indians wore secretive expressions and did not greet me. They seemed to search my face for knowledge of the *pi-eye* dance. I noticed that all signs of the dance had been removed, even to the extent of tearing out by the roots the bushes from which the boy had taken his branches. They had covered the spots with smoothed earth which, however, I detected from its freshness. I think that with a complete stranger in the village they would never have performed the ceremony, simple as it is, even if the patient died without it, although corrupt forms of the dance are performed for visitors by other Indian tribes. For three nights this performance took place. The old man showed no improvement: in fact, by the third day he was much worse, as I had expected. I did not mention what I had seen, but called some of them and pointed out that as the old man was bound to go it would be better to get to work. Their faces remained blank, as dead as the village had been since the dances began, and they refused. No one went out hunting or farther than the edge of their farms.

As the days passed I became desperate, and even began to wish for the old man's death, for nothing could save him and the agony was prolonged for all. Everything depended on his early demise. Eventually his wife came and said that he had not spoken for a long time. She counted the days with her fingers and it was two weeks.

"Now old man talk. He call you. Not Indian, you," she said.

I walked down to see him. The old man slowly turned his eyes to me.

"Rains come, six, seven days. When rains come you look in river. Water will be white. Boy must make fish traps all round village—not by river—round camp."

He turned to Labba, his son, and repeated what he had said to me and ordered him to make the fish *banabu*—literally the fish house. (The same word is used for any place where creatures stay. A bird's nest is a bird *banabu*.)

It seemed impossible that the old man could be right in predicting such an immense rise of water, more than twelve feet, for fish traps to be practical around the village, for the March rains, which might conceivably arrive in a week, were not normally so heavy. The white water was another puzzle, accentuated by the authority of the old man's faltering but oracular tones.

"When rains come," he started again, "you stay in village. Not hunt. Plenty snake."

102

"I will do all things you say," I replied and gripped his shoulder.

I left him to sleep and went to my hut, sure that this night would see his death. I could not help regretting my selfish hopes for it and lay unable to sleep until, at three in the morning, loud wailing suddenly broke out. As I ran down, the girls and even the men began to wail and moan. Labba turned to me and said in bitter tones, as if a thief had been at work:

"Yapung, old man, he gone."

I felt his pulse. It still moved faintly. I held his wrist and twenty minutes later he was dead. I backed away, confused for a moment.

The Indians would have wrapped the old man in his hammock and buried him sitting in a small hole, but I suggested using one of the cassili canoes to close him up securely and hygienically, and they agreed. I hustled them into activity to break the oppressive apathy. Soon they were hammering on the lid furiously, bending nails and splitting the wood. The sobbing old woman pleaded to see his face and I left an aperture at the head.

"Put the lid good," I said, "and the *kanaima*—evil spirit— cannot fly out."

They hammered on, the little children filling the smaller cracks with slivers of wood. Others dug a pit outside the village. We formed a long line, tied a rope to the coffin, and dragged it through the sand, the old woman wailing along behind, stroking the corpse's forehead occasionally. The brusqueness of his removal kept the rest of them calm. Then we rested by the grave and drank some cassili. I covered the old man's face with leaves and nailed on the last section of the lid, and we lowered him in on creeper slings. The earth was shovelled in and I stuck a crude cross over the grave, which I said they must not touch, as it was very good and kept the *kanaima* away.

The old woman's eyes were swollen, her hair bedraggled and her heels muddy from neglect. She severely warned everyone not to touch the cross. The men went back to the old man's

103

house, pulled out his gun, clothes, bows and arrows; everything he had possessed. They broke the gun stock, hammered the barrel, snapped the bows, tore the clothes and flung them out of the village. To my disappointment a well-made tiger-skin cap went the way of the rest and, to make a clean job of it, I made them collect the scattered things and burn them on the grave.

The old woman went to her farm the next day and saw the old man's canoe in the creek. She started crying again. A girl noticed a stone the old man had sat on often, and she also began the dirge. Anything that reminded them of him started it. Sometimes there would be peace for three days; then it would begin again, and so it went on intermittently for three weeks. Some of them went off alone some distance to cry: they moaned the same melody as the dance, but much slower. In this individual mourning none of the others would interfere and they all kept away from the current mourner. The dirge would begin quietly at first from behind some rock and go on for two hours, the voice breaking with sobs. Only then did the real tears flow, this being the one rare occasion on which Indians cry properly. When it was over the Indian would wipe his face and appear in the village as if nothing were amiss. A joke would bring a laugh as easily as before. By encouraging this excessive mourning, and by throwing away all that reminded them of the old man, they brought out the full sorrow of their loss. They kept none of it back so that when it was over the sense of absence in their hearts was healed, once for all. As in his feasting and dancing, the mourning Indian seeks completeness once emotion is aroused.

A week after the burial I decided to look over my kit in preparation for serious prospecting, so one afternoon I pulled out all my mattocks and shovels from the hut. The Indians sat about in the sand by the door chopping out the broken hafts and shaving new ones with their knives. The old woman was stretching my tarpaulin over some bushes to dry it out, as it would be useful on overnight trips. Cassava bread was being baked in the *aki* house for an expedition. I took out my sieves and nailed up the frayed netting. The children ran about playing in the sand as usual, the sun slanting on their bodies and warming the iron tools. One sat naked covering his feet with sand and lifting them out again. Suddenly he looked at the sky.

"*Kanaiti abou,*" he shrilled.

The sky was clear but everyone stopped as the first moistness of misty rain wavered down. I called for all my things to be put inside quickly, and the Indians hurriedly bundled them in and ran off to their huts. By the time they had reached them, black clouds had rolled up and it poured as the old man had predicted. All that night it thundered down. For two and a half days I could not move outside my hut.

I looked out of the window and saw the creek swollen, angry and milky white under a stiff breeze. It roared along just by the village and over the farms, leaving the canoes swinging wildly to their moorings, down to the gunwales with water. The old man had realised that a heavy downpour on the unusually dry clay of the high hills would sweep it down to cause the milky appearance of the flood. When I went down to the village, Labba was busy with twelve or fifteen fish traps which he had made, and put out by the edge of the village. By the third day the river rose to them and the village made a big catch of fish, which made up for the grave shortage of meat due to the poor hunting during the old man's illness and death. Without this catch we would have been hungry, as it was impossible to move from the village across the numerous cataracts that now surrounded it. All this amazed the Indians. They told me that such a flood at this season had not happened for six years. It was like the May rains.

When the rains ceased and the ground steamed I walked to my farm. It took a day for us to cut through the fallen trees. The farm was also a tangle of fallen trees, which had collapsed from the edges of the clearing. A number of banana trees and much of the green shooting crops were broken down, but there had been no erosion of the soil, as the farm stood on a well-drained slope. The trees were too wet to burn and we had to cut them up with my axes and their knives—the hardest work

105

that had been done on the farm. But I felt that the worst was over and that surely now I could get away quickly to find the much-needed diamonds. The rains would help me, as I could survey the creeks while the waters still ran, and see their true channels. In them would be my first search. I suggested this to Labba and he said it was "good, very good."

Once more the prospecting stores came out for hurried repairs. The Indians had been refreshed by the rain, which seemed to cut off the disagreeable past and conjure up a fresh future for them. I told them frankly that I had ammunition to last only one more hunt. Actually I had eight flasks·of powder hidden away in case food ran short. I had brought with me a hundred rounds of ammunition, and many brass cases of different gauges to fit the Indians' guns, as well as caps and bags of shot and flasks of powder. The brass cases could be used over again by knocking out the fired cap with a nail and recharging according to preference. The open end of the cases I stuffed with bits of old newspaper. This method is more practicable in the jungle than taking large quantities of cardboard cartridges, which are expensive, swell so that they cannot fit the guns, and often leave one short of the weight of cartridge most required. There are many such tricks for successful jungle life and I had already discovered that they could not be learnt quickly.

So it was arranged that we would go out with all the braves and make one big hunt along the creeks and that I would look for my treasure. I told them of the plenty of cloth, beads, flour, sugar, salt, powder and guns I could buy for them if I was successful. Amou and Labba grinned and all of them beamed cheerfully. I locked my hut and told the women to clear up the remaining mess on the farm, as I would be gone about three weeks. The old woman called to me as we straggled out of the village laden with *warishis*:

"Which line you taking?"

"To mountains that way," I said, and pointed south.

She said that she had a plan: the women could carry supplies down to us to avoid the need to send men back to the village for cassava bread. We agreed on this and said we would mark the ten-mile trail as we went so that they could follow us easily. This is almost automatic for Indians, who walk along swinging their knives, slicing a branch here and there. There were also the horns which could be blown by either party. I told her to make the trips every seven days to arrive when we would be resting.

Amou, Labba, John, and three other youths made up my party and we set off at once. Two of the youths were the new boys who had married into the village. They had never been out prospecting before and were eager to learn. Both of them were good shots for small game. The seven of us were fully armed, as we were going into thick jungle, where tapir were so plentiful that there were bound to be either spotted tigers or large deer tigers after them. The fawn-coloured deer tigers are cunning and need watching.

A slight drizzle fell and the morning was chilly as we plodded along with the *warishis* creaking at our backs. For the first mile we did not bother to blaze a trail as the ground was fairly open and our footprints showed. Mist hung on the ground, waist high, appearing like a rainbow, to move ahead always at the same distance, so that for ten yards around one seemed to be standing in a pool surrounded by shards of white. We hurried on, determined to reach the camp site before nightfall in one march. We came to swampy country but did not try to save time by going through it, as there were too many large pythons. Being well-laden we did not wish to meet a danger which at other times would have been no problem to experienced hunters. Pythons are not quick in attack but are sure in their movements. They appear to think before attacking and strike the victim when he is in the most unfavourable situation, and their greatest weapon is the terror they inspire. As we began to come out of the fringe of swamp we saw evidence of this.

Amou was leading and held up his hand: wild pig were grazing ahead. We thrust our heads carefully through the bushes and watched them. Just then I saw a python, about twenty-five feet long, slithering along the edge of the grass, partly concealed from the pig. One large boar stood apart from the others. The snake raised its head and looked about it, then slid round the small clearing in which the pig stood and disappeared for a few moments. Again it came in sight, still viewing the situation. It seemed to pay particular attention to a leaning tree. The boar was becoming restive as the strong smell of the python wafted over: all snakes smell distinctively and Indians are forewarned yards beforehand, being able to state what particular snake is ahead, so that they are rarely bitten. To those with trained noses, even a millipede gives itself away by a strong stench. Some snakes smell of peach, others have a ratty smell. Generally, smells are more informative in the jungle than sounds.

The python saw the boar raise its tusks and grunt, and the snake slid swiftly to one side and rushed at running speed over the twenty feet separating it from him. The boar hopped round, lifting its huge bulk daintily, but the python struck the back legs before the turn was complete. The pig was thrown off balance and staggered. Like an oiled corkscrew the python coiled round the hind part of the pig; when it had given two turns round the body it constricted steadily. The boar roared and saliva dripped from its mouth, as it heaved about, lifting six or seven feet of the grey python. But the grip tightened and the front legs of the boar gradually ceased to thrash. Apparently having sensed that the pig was unconscious, the python continued corkscrewing round the body, wrapping even the legs in its coils. In a few moments I heard the cracking sound of breaking bones as if someone were breaking a bundle of sticks. The python uncoiled and withdrew from the pig, which was now shapeless, with dull bruise marks the size of plates. The python raised its head and opened its mouth which gradually distended, so that the lips were almost in one line and the orifice sprung wider, like rubber. It applied its distended mouth to the rear of the pig like a small boy sticking a rubber suction cup to a ball. I could see the sides of its mouth beginning to work: the teeth hinging back to allow the pig to pass. Slime oozed from the sides of the mouth as the snake reached the boar's stomach. We watched the python for about twenty minutes and did not wait to see more.

The Indians had told me that if one is caught by a python the best defence is a slanting scythe blow on the back with a keen heavy hunting knife. If struck true, the blade will slip between the tough scales and paralyse the python. But the blow has to be swift and made as a slash. Fortunately a python rarely attacks a man in open ground: only the biggest would risk the encounter. If the man shows fight, the python will probably try and frighten him into thickets where he can corner his victim and gain an anchorage on a small tree with his tail, so it is best to keep one's nerve and stay in the open.

After this revolting spectacle, I said that we had come quite a distance and that we should make a trail. They shook their heads and pointed behind us and I saw that they had been walking in short grass and soft earth with their heels, which left the necessary marks every three or four yards. Every now and then they purposely went through mud. Such prints will show for at least ten days, unless there is heavy rain. After six hours' walk we reached the sandstone hills I had aimed at, where we unloaded the *warishis* and unpacked the cassava bread, shovels, picks, mattocks and my personal kit.

We were in open ground on the banks of a shallow creek. The surface gravel looked promising, so there we camped. I said that we would all sleep under my tarpaulin, as it would take some time to build separate shelters, but, unfortunately, I had not reckoned with the smell that gradually grew under that tarpaulin when the men began to hang their haunches of meat around their hammocks and started constant, smoky fires. Next morning I went along the creek probing by the stick method. During the next six days we covered a lot of ground, making small prospect holes whenever there were good signs. I found plenty of carbon and small shreds of mica among loose stones, which were encouraging: the diamond friends, as the Indians called them. There were also indications of gold. Yet it had been such a dreamy existence in the village, where everything seemed to look after itself, that I was tempted to give up the back-breaking work to laze in a hammock. I had to curb impatience as well as laziness. This time I was determined to be thorough and make a strike. But the Indian habit prevailed, and sometimes we lay all day long doing nothing.

On the Sunday following our arrival I looked around the creek. Already the tarpaulin had a well-established look, sagging slightly, with the hammocks in the deep cool shadow beneath. Around were water gourds and the ashes of fires. *Warishis* lay where they had been dropped, with some shovels lying against them. I heard three of the men splashing in the water of the creek. The young boys were counting out cartridges to go on a short hunt. I picked up my sieves without any plan in mind and wandered off. In about ten minutes I found myself beside a small "sag," which was a minor tributary of the main creek. To a depth of about a foot the bed was choked with rotting leaves, twigs and stumps, so I took a stick and cleared a patch of it. I sounded with my wand and found very loose gravel. I would not have thought of gravel in such an unlikely place, but it might have been a water drainage from a sand patch and nothing more. I went back for a shovel, and when I dug down I found black gravel. I flung it in the sieve and went to the running water of the creek. I washed away: there was nothing in the first sieve nor in the second, but in the bottom one there was a sudden shot of light. I climbed back on the bank and picked out a diamond. I turned it over carefully and estimated that it was ninety-eight points, just less than one carat. I was so excited that I immediately put a price on it of ten pounds sterling. Most of its surface was coated green by vegetation, with small brown spots probably from the gravel in which it had lain. But it was absolutely clean: I could detect not a single flaw nor injury. I recalled my diamond-cutting days and all sorts of calculations flashed through my mind. From this one stone I could buy a month's supply, if I bought carefully. That was the delight of it.

I decided that this was the spot where I would really work. I put the stone in an empty cartridge case, which seemed the best way to keep it. It would be my secret "kitty," as prospectors call their diamond cache. I hurried back to camp and found the men roasting the birds they had shot. They tasted delicious but I had no appetite: greedy visions of handfuls of flashing stones drove my mind on a hectic repetitive treadmill. I did not dare think it might be the only one I would find. I slept badly and next morning told the men to bring all the tools down to the small sag.

When Labba and Amou saw the hole I had made they looked at me and smiled.

"Find diamond? Find diamond?"

"No," I said. "Diamond *yapung tukay, tukay*—but many, many signs of them!"

I decided to tell them nothing about my find, lest they felt enough had been won. They tried to estimate how diamonds could possibly lie in this backwater, since stones must roll from the mountains. They could not believe that any could have swung in here. However I persuaded them to prepare to clear the sag, which was about a hundred yards long. First I got them to fell all the small trees at the side, for the ground would have to be opened for efficient work. All the rocks were levered out and the stagnant water drained. It took us two days to clear everything, including the leaves, from forty feet of the sag and then the light sand, four inches thick, was revealed. In this way I hoped that the job would be done methodically. I feared that if the Indians began in their way to dig hurriedly here and there we might be lucky, but we would probably also lose many stones in the turmoil of gravel.

I made a wooden platform on the bank near the main creek and covered it with a layer of smooth deep sand, on which they dumped the gravel by a bucket chain. We dug all day, perspiring in the pits, which went down to green clay. From the diggings I reckoned the gravel went straight up into the hill, so we scraped the clay carefully to a depth of an inch below it. When we had a good pile of it on the platform, they made a leaf shelter above in case of rain. The third day's work was my sole responsibility and I set about washing the whole heap alone, except for one man who brought the gravel to me at the creek in buckets. The others I sent to clear the next section of the sag.

Only one problem existed; our supplies were low and the women had not arrived, although it was the second week of our stay. I could not afford at this stage to spare men to return to the village and wondered what had held up the women. However everyone by this time was excited enough to go hungry. I set up a prominent kitty by hanging a cartridge case on a tree branch, into which went all the small stones I found. When I washed the gravel and found a small one, I made a great play with it in the sieve so that they saw it. I would call them and they would crowd round laughing and examining it closely, holding it up to the sun.

But I kept my secret kitty in my pocket and put all big stones in it. I found eleven as well as many small ones: broken, "cleavages," "industrials" and rejects. Some were "tailor chalks," shaped like the flat triangular chalk used by tailors to mark cloth. At the end of a week's work I had about ten carats of stones—a good "take." Frequently I got away from the others, pulled out my kitty, spread a handkerchief on my hand and threw them out, just to look at them. Sometimes I felt frustrated at being unable to pull them out on impulse and play with them. At these times I would put my hand nonchalantly into my pocket and uncork the kitty to spill them into my fingers and feel them secretly.

At last two girls arrived with heavy *warishis* of food.

"Any diamonds found?" was their first question. They let the strap free from their heads and shook their hair back.

"Yes, plenty small ones. No big ones," said Labba.

"No good. No good," Amou added.

I was happy to let them think so: they would have stopped work at once if they had known of my real find. The girls only stayed half an hour before setting back to the village. I made sure they did not delay, as one of them was the wife of one of the new boys; if she had stayed it would have delayed work.

We continued clearing out the sag and when it was finished I had fifteen carats. There were fewer diamonds in the upper stretch. I concluded that the hill had thrown the stones into the sag and that most of them had gone into the creek. It was fairly obvious that at the sag mouth and in the main creek would lie the real treasure, but I had not worked the mouth properly as it sank quickly into deep water. Looking at the lie of the creek and the stone drifts on the bottom, I thought that the bend just below the mouth of the sag would be the best place. As it happened, I never worked that creek, and to this day there is a pocket of diamonds waiting there, perhaps four or five times the amount I took from the sag, including bigger and cleaner stones. Diamonds found in running water are nearly always good. That is why the "water" diamonds of South America are renowned.

However, time was pressing. Packing up we hurried back to the village, shooting some game on the way, which was set up for smoking as soon as we arrived. I greeted the others as perfunctorily as I could. My only desire was to get to my hut, shut the door, open the little window and have a really good look at my find. I told the boys we would rest for a few days and then make the long trip to the frontier for supplies. I said I would be in my hut and did not want to be disturbed, and although it was unusual for me to rest all day they accepted my explanation of tiredness. Once inside, I shut the door, opened the little window, spread an old magazine on the bench, threw out the diamonds and began to clean them. I estimated their value, bearing in mind that any Brazilian "pirate" buyers I might meet would be shrewd and would give me no more than a quarter of the stones' real value. I thought I would be satisfied if I made £100 on them, although in a genuine market they might have fetched about £400. If I cut them myself, which I could do with the expensive equipment I kept at home, their value would be in the region of £600. Such is the order of difference in diamond prices, according to the market dealt in. The smallest return would satisfy me, however, as I wanted to come back as soon as possible to the creeks. I again parcelled the diamonds, this time in three lots: the big ones, the smaller clean ones and the industrials. On any occasion I could pick the right grade for display.

Preparations were now going ahead for the trip to the frontier, as I wanted to leave as soon as possible. Excitement spread at once. It appeared to be a good thing to arrange six or seven such events during the year to keep up their enthusiasm. Then suddenly I thought of the danger of having my claim jumped while I was away. It is not unknown for dealers to keep a prospector talking while they send a man back up his trail, or they might even bribe a half-civilised frontier Indian to find out where I had been. I called Labba and Amou and we almost ran back to the sag. We blazed the trees around the claim and I set up boards with my name and date. When I reached the post office at Orinduik I would stake an official claim by registered letter to the Commissioner of Lands and Mines: for an area of about fifteen hundred feet by eight hundred feet, the licence would be a pound sterling a year. Although it would not give me complete protection, it was better than leaving the ground open. In the whole region of the Pakaraimas, which cover an area of more than 15,000 square miles, there are only a few prospectors and most of them operate in certain well-defined areas near well-known camps. Few go as far as I had gone into Indian country. But news travels surprisingly quickly and I could not take any more chances than were necessary. Fortunately the claim I was to make lay just inside British territory, so that buying a licence was a practical proposition. I knew now, at least, that if the Indians were asked they would be able to say that I had cut lines and put up boards, which would be some discouragement to prospective claim-jumpers.

We arrived back at the village late that night, and next day I called on Amou and John to accompany me to the frontier. We were to travel light and I arranged that another party would follow us in a fortnight, to meet us near the frontier and take the supplies back to the village.

CHAPTER SEVEN

The Bargain

WE set off at a rapid pace, dispensed with early nights and
comfortable camps and, leaving the main trails used by loaded
men, made many short cuts across rocky country. Late at night,
when I could march no farther, we tied our hammocks up
carelessly, and fell asleep; some nights we merely propped ourselves in the crooks of trees. The weather was dry, otherwise
this casualness would have been impossible. We reached the
surroundings of Orinduik about mid-April. There was still a
fortnight before the rains were due, but I reckoned that the

heavy rains which had fallen at the time of the old man's death would delay those in May.

As we approached Orinduik I found that all the old trails had become overgrown, and although I knew the area I could not have found my way without the Indians. John knew Orinduik, but Amou had never been to "civilisation." As far as I knew, I approached the settlement unknown to anyone. Then he turned a corner and I saw a short, thick-set figure approaching along the trail, a pistol hanging at his waist and a battered Panama clinging to the back of his tousled head. I dramatically slipped the safety catch on my gun in case of a hold-up; they are not unknown, especially on the Brazilian side of the frontier.

He was a bearded "pirate" wearing an open khaki shirt, with no buttons, out of which sprouted a mass of black hair. At his back he carried a small pack, in which, I suspected, would be his diamond scales and a bottle of rum. As we drew near he beamed at me and we greeted him but kept our hands free. He stopped squarely in front of me, blocking the trail, the sweat trickling down his fat neck.

"Want a drink?" he asked in Portuguese.

I imagined that he wanted me drunk to make me an easy customer. Already I was acting like a suspicious Indian! When I refused, he produced the bottle and swigged a quarter of neat rum, corked it, and cocked his head on one side inquiringly.

"Going for rations," I said warily, and then added on a silly impulse, "have a fine lot of diamonds." If there was to be bargaining, I might as well praise my wares: he would be sure to say they were no good. I turned to John and Amou, who were standing behind me:

"You go down the trail and see no one comes," I said to Amou, and told John to stand a little distance off and keep an eye on the bargaining. I spoke rapidly in Patamona and they moved off.

I looked at the pirate, who was producing another beaming smile, and nodded to a fallen tree. We sat astride it, facing each other, I keeping my gun across my knee with one hand and feeling for my caches with the other. There was no signal

116

from Amou, and I felt fairly certain that none of the smiler's friends were peering at me from the jungle.

"All right," I said, as calmly as I could, "let's do business."

It was like a first game of poker for high stakes: we sat watching each other between oily glances and I sensed that beneath his smile and plumpness the smiler was no easy bargainer. His eyes were starting out of his head as he darted glances at my pocket. He took off his haversack and opened it on the ground. I pulled out the first kitty and held it up and rattled the small stones. He shook his head still smiling.

"Oh," he groaned in mock despair, adding in bad Portuguese, "*valnade, valnade*—no good at all."

I smiled as confidently as I could and gave him the kitty. He poured the stones into his hand and with hardly a glance rubbed them over once.

"I give you forty-two dollars." He gleamed generously.

"O.K."

I took out the second kitty and shook it.

"Better, uh? Uh?"

"*Si,*" I drawled professionally.

He wiped the back of his hand across his mouth, tipped back his hat and took a better grip of the log with his thighs. He held out his hand expectantly, but I turned the stones into my own. He beamed.

"You weigh them," I said.

"No, I give you good average."

He was robbing me, but I knew that if I insisted on the scales he would slash the prices to nothing.

He looked at the stones.

"I give you . . ." He thought and rubbed his chin, looked again and pawed them over once more. He closed his hands. His eyes shot up under his thick lashes.

"You have big ones, uh?" He smiled.

"Maybe."

"You tell me. Go on, you tell me." He scratched his neck.

If I say I have big ones, I thought, he may give me a hot price for the middle lot.

"Yes," I said finally. "Good ones, big ones."

"Oh." He breathed, looking at me half sideways. He did not know whether to believe me.

"All right, I give you . . ." Again a pause to look at the stones and the jungle. He was estimating whether this was his last buy; he wanted to avoid doing himself out of a fine profit.

"O.K. I give you eighty-three dollars this lot."

That made one hundred and twenty-five dollars for the two lower grades—about thirty-two pounds sterling. I began to figure what I could get in the final and biggest sale: they were worth twice the value of the other two kitties together. He counted out the money and handed it over with a smile; then with a quick jerk he flung all my stones into his open haversack among a lot of his stones.

I opened the last kitty and the stones shone handsomely.

"Oh! Well!" he sighed and smiled. Suddenly he seemed deflated and lost interest in the stones. He talked about prices being down. There were all sorts of reasons, apparently, why big stones were not in demand.

He looked at the stones one by one.

"If you don't give me a good price now," I said, "I will keep the lot."

"No," he said, "small ones mix up already. Can't get them back." I looked at the haversack and saw that my small stones were mingled with his, beyond recovery. As he took the big ones in his hand I took a firmer grip on my gun: I was quite prepared to fire should he run.

He gave me a big, reassuring smile.

"I have little time," I said. "I must go for supplies."

He looked keenly at me and half closed his eyes. The smile faded.

"I give you three hundred dollars," he said solemnly as if he were offering his soul.

"I have no time. I go to Tesserik." Tesserik was the chief storekeeper in Orinduik.

"No. No. You sell!" His eyebrows worked. The name

118

Tesserik had thrown him off balance. He tweaked his hat brim and rustled the forest on his chest.

"Three-fifty."

"Look," I grumbled, "you make plenty of fun now."

He had in fact reached the figure I had aimed at. I mentioned that I had the Indians to pay and there was plenty of work to get back to my claim. If I went to Tesserik, I said, I would get a better price—as well as credit for supplies. He thought for a moment.

"How far you work?"

This seemed to be going too far: I imagined my claim being jumped.

"Somewhere that side," I said, waving at Brazil and Venezuela.

He looked round at John.

"Oh, Patamona."

"Patamona all about," I pointed out. "At Boa Vista, Santa Maria, Orinduik, Ireng and most in the mountains."

"All right. You good customer. I give you three-fifty." He smiled. We were back where we had been three minutes before.

"Look," I said, "I want four hundred. Finish. I promise you next two months I bring another set of diamonds I have in my camp. I will come out again for big supplies," I lied.

"Sure? O.K., I give you four hundred. Extra fifty because of the promise, not for the diamonds."

He counted out four hundred British dollars and immediately shook all the diamonds together in his haversack. He pulled out the rum again and held it up.

"No thanks, I am going to get supplies," I said, swinging off the log.

"O.K. I get you everything," he persisted.

I told him what I wanted. It would come to six hundred pounds weight, mostly of flour and sugar. He calculated quickly.

"Come to around four-five hundred dollars," he said. The cost would in fact be about two hundred and fifty.

"No," I said. "Tesserik."

Apart from losing business, he wanted no wind of his

presence to get to the police as, like other pirates, he had no licence. So he left the price and asked me to see what he had.

I called John and Amou and followed him. About half a mile down the trail he had a little hut, secreted in the jungle, where two other men were cooking over a small fire. The business was over, and the smiler and his men became courteous hosts, offering me a meal. They gave Amou and John cigarettes and suggested whisky, but I would not allow it.

One of them said he was looking for work and asked if I had a position to offer. I evaded this, as it sounded like another trap. But it was all conducted in a friendly spirit. Smiler said he would get all I required and he went behind some bushes where he had several oxen laden with all kinds of goods. He must have been wandering through the frontier regions bartering as he went along. I would not have been surprised to discover that he had rustled the oxen on the way: when they were worked out, he would probably take them to a prospecting camp and kill them for sale as beef.

After an hour's further bargaining, we reached acceptable figures. I bought a drum of salted biscuits, cloth bolts, beads, many flasks of powder and bags of shot, and other things. It left me with about ninety dollars in cash and I was sure that I had paid three times the value of several items. The next problem was to take my goods and make a clean get-away. The men from the village would not be at the rendezvous for another day or so and I did not relish the idea of waiting for them with only Amou and John, although the three of us would have been a match for the dealers by themselves. I asked them to pack my goods on their oxen and carry them some distance along the trail: they were willing to do anything, as they expected me back in two months. Apparently they did not realise that in two months the place where they stood would be flooded.

It was pleasant staying that night in their camp. In the evening the bottle was passed round, they brought out their guitars and one of them sang. There was plenty of good food and cigarettes. I had bought a new hammock from them for thirty dollars and Amou, John and I slept one above the other with the hammocks on the same branch. It was merely a precaution: I did not believe that the pirates meant trouble and, at any rate, there was none. We all rose early and they served coffee with biscuits, bread and butter, which to us was a great luxury.

On the excuse of having to send a registered letter home, I went in to Orinduik alone and registered the claim. When I returned all the oxen were loaded and the Brazilians said they would take me for a couple of miles along the trail, which suited me, as the party from the village would be thereabouts in two days or so. When we reached the place we unloaded and they asked if the Indians were coming. To hurry them off I said they would arrive when the sun was high.

"Maybe two months time prices will be a little better," said Smiler at our parting.

We all shook hands and they led away the empty oxen. Now I had to wait until the villagers came: I dared not hide the stores and go on at once. Amou, John and I set up a small camp, but we were careful not to make a big fire as I did not want to broadcast evidence of our stay. I moved the supplies further into the jungle and sent John to set up camp by himself in the mountains to scout for the other Indians. The hours dragged and we waited in the camp for three days, unwilling to venture far from the stores and hunt. We did not talk much and spent most of the time eating. Amou made no remarks about the Brazilians: I had talked very fast and he found the various moves and bargaining somewhat confusing. All he would say was:

"Me know. Brazilian. He wear this *alouk*." He pointed to his head, referring to the Panama hat.

"I see them many years ago. They go about with *pyala* —the cows—on the frontier with many things."

Finally the party of five arrived from the hills. There was no resting, and the *warishis* were loaded at once. I kept the ammunition in my *warishi*, carrying about forty pounds in all. We set off back on the trail and, after several days, came to a river crossing. In the camp that night I realised that May was already upon us, and when the men told me that there had been a little rain in the village before they left I became afraid of our being caught in downpours which would spoil the stores. In order to lighten the *warishis*, therefore, we unloaded half the weight of the goods and I sent off the party from the village, which departed as fast as it could to reach the village and return. The rest of us were to follow more slowly with the heavy stuff, and the rear party stayed that day by the river. During the night there was some slight rain and the river rose three feet. Events were soon to show how foolish my tactics were, for if I had gone on with the whole party there would have been none of the trouble that came upon us, beginning with the rise in the river, which was just enough to prevent us passing over easily.

Next day the river went down slightly and the Indians urged a quick crossing. We made a rough raft, using the tarpaulin to wrap up the goods, and reached the other side in good order. On the opposite bank we stacked the stores on high ground, about fifteen feet above the river. I made my next mistake by ordering on the rest of the men with another lot of goods. I said that I would wait with the last things until they returned with the full strength of the village to take the goods quickly onward. My hope was that if we carried light loads of about twenty pounds each, we would be able to swim with them across the numerous creeks in our path, should it be necessary. Amou did not want to leave me, but after some persuasion he agreed to go. The party carried thirty pounds each and would, I hoped, make a rapid journey. When they had gone, I settled down to wait. The days passed; finally a week had gone by without a sign of anyone, and I became anxious. Now I thought of my own existence but could not summon the courage to go hunting alone. The farthest I would go was about a mile from the camp, and eventually on this short round I shot two powice.

Towards the end of the week the rains had begun to break and I built a small camp of leaves, a quick job if one knows how.

For days the rain came heavily, the river rose, and from my shelter I could hear the rapids roaring. A quarter of one bag of sugar became waterlogged from rain driving through the side of the shelter, so I transferred the dry sugar to another bag and left it near the fire. Then I stacked the rest of the goods round the fire, including the salt, which I hoped to keep hard. I looked out towards the river occasionally and reckoned that even if it came in full flood I would be clear of it, for the camp was twenty yards from the water on the lower spur of a conglomerate ironstone hill, well above the high-water marks on the boulders and large trees. As the rain increased I ate into the rations and wrapped my cartridges inside my shirt with rolls of cloth round me. They were my most valuable goods.

After three days of rain I felt cramping pains from sitting and sleeping half crouched under the shelter. I was short of sleep and frequently woke to the sound of the rushing water, the white foam of which I could now see from my position. As I was on a bend in the river the water seemed to be around me. I was worried about the Indians: if they had made a good twenty miles through the creeks they would have reached easier country, and I hoped they had done so without abandoning any stores. As none returned I imagined they had got through, but clearly the big party coming for me could not reach my camp in such weather: I was cut off from the village for the duration of the rains. Although the problem now was simply how I was to recross the river and get back to the frontier, I was in two minds and hoped that I might still find a way to the village, even if I had to leave most of the stores.

But I was beginning to feel weak from living on sugar, flour and water and lacked the power of firm decision. A fire was no longer possible and my hammock was always damp and I had shivering fits. The river kept on rising. Finally I decided to find a higher spot and move the stores into a new camp. Eventually one morning I found a dry and sheltered ledge on a bluff about twenty feet high, surrounded by thorny bushes, which I spent six hours cutting out. The prospect of carrying the heavy sacks up to this point was depressing: I might carry them up painfully in a day only to have to carry them down again. I thought I would stay under the ledge with essential stores and leave the rest, at least for the time being.

Nights I went to the ledge and lit a fire from the dry thorn bushes. I slept soundly but still wanted fresh meat to build up my strength. Now was my opportunity to put into practice all that I had learnt among the Indians. One day at noon the sun showed slightly, although the wind and dripping trees caused as great a downpour in the jungle as rain. However, it was a good time to hunt, as my feet made no noise over the sodden leaves, so I set off, taking clear directions towards prominent trees, and blazed the trail quietly. Every now and then I stopped to listen and look back to make sure I could recognise the trail: it was easy, but I was apprehensive.

I saw nothing to shoot, not even a small toucan. Feeling tired, I sat on a fallen mora tree and waited to see if any birds came to feed around me in the sand. Nearly three hours had passed since I had left camp and I was hungry. I thought I would make one bold skirmish through the jungle to shoot something, being sure that eventually I would come across my trail and find my way back, so I started cutting my way through the thick undergrowth and pushed on for almost an hour. I could still hear the rushing of the river, but now there was a new sound of water nearby. I broke through the trees and found a small creek dashing along at an angle towards the main river.

From the lie of the land I realised that the creek was an overflow from the river behind me and ran to join up a great loop in the main stream. Soon the part where I stood would be flooded. I listened for some time and heard water running, not only in front of me, but behind. Somewhere back on the trail another overflow creek had begun to run. I climbed to the top of a mound by the creek and estimated that I was six feet above the stream. Since the creek was obviously normally dry, it seemed impossible that the water could reach the top of the mound, but I decided in any case to walk down the stream and see if there was an outlet along its banks which would take the water off and keep it low. The creek at that time was only two feet deep. After clambering along the banks for some time, I found no outlet. I lost all sense of danger and the need for alertness in my hunger and exhaustion and was careless of the sound of water around me.

I began to crash through the forest, hurriedly kicking aside stumps and pushing back branches to clear my path. Indians would never move like this: the risk of startling a snake is too great. I strapped my gun on my shoulder and forgot hunting. In my headlong passage I might have been trampling through an English wood to catch the last train. But my concern was really more serious—I wanted to get back to my stores and bring as much as I could up to the creek. Then if I had to cross it quickly, everything would be to hand. My plan would be to make a small raft and push my stores across to the other side.

As soon as I reached the camp under the ledge, I lit a fire and cooked a meal and then lay in my hammock smoking and thinking out my situation and becoming fatally undecided once more. It was late in the evening, and I dozed off and slept right through the night as the rain poured down, and it was still coming down in torrents at eight in the morning when I awoke with alarm. The fire was nearly out but I was warm in my hammock. I noticed that the rushing and pounding of water had ceased and except for the rain there was no sound in the jungle. Peace seemed to have returned, and I imagined that the river must have found outlets lower down to take off the flood. I fell back into a daze, rolled out of my hammock and took my time strapping my gun on my shoulder to walk down to the main stores. The leaves beneath my feet were sopping wet and eventually the water squelched above my shoes. I glanced ahead and saw a sheet of water. The stores were nowhere to be seen. The river had risen so high that all sound of strife had ceased. The highest boulders were covered in the smooth, glacial flow of a deep, embracing flood.

I paddled into it and discovered the stores in water as high as my chest. Beneath the surface I made out the wavering white shape of the flour sack; the sugar was there also, but all the tinned stores had been washed away. I slung my gun on a tree, took off my clothes, and jumped into the moving water. Holding on to a pole left from the wreck of the shelter, I dived down and tried to pull up the flour, but it was too heavy to surface. With my knife I slit the bag at the base and kicked it: lumps of flour bobbed up and I grabbed them and carried them to a dry rock. I dived again for my haversack, which contained medical stores. Somewhere nearby I knew the boxes of tinned goods must be, but the water towards the river flowed more swiftly, timber swept by, and it was too deep and difficult to dive for them. I concentrated on the sugar and, after repeated dives, I brought a few handfuls of liquid sugar to the rock.

I pulled out a tin I kept in my haversack for thread, needles, razor blades and so on, and emptied it to hold the sugar. A bottle in which I kept beads was also emptied into the flood. It was washed and packed with the flour. By now I only thought of a quick escape and of my task. Clumsily I scraped the rest of the flour from the rock with a good seasoning of sand and mixed a dough. Before the flood rose again I decided to make a fire and bake it, so, carrying a small stock of damp goods, I splashed back to the ledge and blew up the fire. The ledge camp was now an island and I knew that I would have to swim out of the encircling floods.

As soon as they were done, I ate two of the bakes and put the rest in a scarf slung round my neck. I unloaded the gun, wrapped up all my remaining powder and shot and put them inside my shirt. Strapping my gun high on my shoulder, I paddled into the water, which quickly rose above my waist to my neck. I moved carefully in the direction of the stream. Landmarks were covered and frequently I slipped into deep pools. When I reached swift water I knew I was at the stream: it was six to eight feet deep. I climbed up until the water was shallow enough to strap on my haversack and gun more tightly. Then I jumped in to swim to the other side, but I was swung round in circles and turned head over heels several times. Finally I allowed the current to sweep me along, and soon felt branches beneath my feet, when I became afraid that the stream was so deep and powerful that I might be swept on into the river.

I sank my head in the water and the haversack on my back acted as a lifebelt. Pulling strongly with my free left hand, I swung myself into a backwater and surfaced. Unaccountably, blood was streaming from my nose. I grabbed a simatou vine without caring about the piercing thorns and slowly pulled myself out of the flood up the vine to a sapling, but when I tried to climb I found I was too heavy to rise and the sapling bent over. I let go of the vine and swung from the sapling towards another tree. It was more than an hour of struggle before my feet touched ground once more and I emerged with water streaming out of my packages and blood oozing from many cuts.

Soon I was walking in shallow water, and when the ground appeared I ran ahead for forty minutes or so, finally reaching a patch of sand where I flung off my traps, slumped down and lay for what seemed hours in the soaking rain. Nothing mattered now that I felt solid ground. I buried my hands in the sand and enjoyed the faint warmth stored beneath. Finally I looked at myself and tried to pull out some of the thorns. I walked back the way I had come and washed in the first pool of water, inspected my stores and found the bakes wet but the sugar and flour safe in their containers. Some of the cartridges were damp, but the powder flask, of course, was watertight, these flasks being like smaller versions of the metal water-bottles used by troops, but with a tiny nipple at the neck from which an accurate measure of powder can be poured. Each flask holds about half a pound and they are the only practical means of carrying powder in tropical jungle. My hammock was soaked, although I had rolled it up tightly and strapped it at the back of my neck, so I unrolled it and strung it between the trees, where, despite the slight drizzle, I hoped the strong breeze would help to dry it out.

Then I looked about for palm leaves to build a shelter. I

intended to camp for a couple of days and rest and, if the water went down, to swim the creek and go back to find some of the tinned stores. As I sat by the fire that night I pondered on what I should do then. Half my stores were lost, including the goods for the Indians. I wondered what they would do with the goods they had taken to the village. They might come back to look for me or forget me altogether. I trusted them, but could not foresee their moves nor plan my own. As evening drew on I realised that there was no sign of the flood going down, but I waited another two days in faint hope, and eventually it began to drop, but too slowly. All my supplies were finished. I had nothing except my gun and ammunition, but all game had fled far from the flooded land.

I curbed my imagination, loaded six cartridges, put my haversack and hammock on my back and set off for the frontier, listening for gunfire or any other sign of man; but heard nothing. The Indians had not come back. I strapped my hand with the cloth which had held the bakes and took my knife to blaze the trail, following the river bank as closely as I could and keeping watch for a crossing to get back on the frontier side. For the whole day I marched. One rapid succeeded another and there was no place to cross, but just as evening came I found a great pool of still water, where the river piled up behind two massive boulders. Through the gap, no more than three feet wide, the water spouted in a roaring jet to the stream below. I climbed over boulders through tangled roots until I was over the inner side of the fall where the water was deep and slow. As it was dry ground, I kept watch for snakes seeking shelter there. By this time I had fully regained control of myself and tried to imagine how an Indian would escape from being cornered without food in a flood.

I put down my baggage, set my gun by a tree ready to fire and took my knife to cut a light wood raft, but on many of the trees my knife bounced off the wet, springy bark. I walked further into the forest and chose some wild banana plants: with a dozen of them I was sure I could make a raft sufficient at

128

least to carry my stores and my gun. I carried the banana trunks to the river side and went in again to find vine rope. I laid eight trunks together, put four above them crosswise and one at each end, binding all securely. In the gaps I packed green leaves and the result was a shaky platform, so I cut hardwood spikes and drove them through the bananas to stiffen the raft. I tied a long bushrope to one end of the raft and eased it into the water. It floated with a few inches freeboard, sinking easily with a little pressure, so I pulled it out and built a small platform in the centre from hardwood branches. On this I laid the gun and the bag. The painter was tied to a small tree to prevent the raft from being carried through the waterfall.

I undressed, put my clothes on the raft and pushed it gently into the river. Swimming slowly alongside, I edged it towards the gap in the boulders, keeping close to the stone. I moved very slowly to prevent any stir or sudden movement that might throw me into the spout. The raft bobbed along, hitting the end of the boulder and bobbing away again. After half an hour's painstaking work, I realised that I could not give the raft the momentum to shoot across the gap. Something was holding it back and I began to suspect the line, which had remained below the surface. I felt with my toes and found that it ran under me in a loop, thrumming with the water pressure. It was caught in the spout and held the raft like a sea-anchor. I took my knife from the raft and pulled back to the slack water where I dived and cut the line, while holding the raft steady with the other hand.

The operation then became simple. With a long shove the raft glided across the gap and caught in the side of the opposite boulder. I plunged after it with the cut painter, put on my pants and a scarf over my shoulder to take the gun sling, and with my haversack on my back, I set off again. I estimated that if I struck straight in for eight miles I would hit one of the many trails into the frontier, and so reach the Brazilians.

I made sure as I blazed the trail that I took a straight route, frequently looking back at the marks to see that I was striking directly from the river.

I walked fast in the remaining hour of daylight and soon came across some sauri nuts buried in the top-soil. The thick shell is the size of an orange; the nut the size of a walnut, and sweet. The sauri nut, I remembered, is the haunt of the labaria snake, as the nuts are a favourite food of many small animals and labarias sometimes set a trap by piling up the nuts and lying under them. The Indians had often warned me when picking sauris to roll them over first with a stick. So I chose only those lying isolated and on the surface. I munched my first meal that day and then heard the first sound, the bellowing of a cow.

The going had been easy and I estimated that I had walked three or four miles. It may be, I thought, that the cow belongs to the Brazilians, but just then darkness fell and made further search difficult. With mounting hope, I collected some brushwood and made a fire at the base of a large tree so that the fire faced ahead into the jungle. I wrapped all the spare rags and scarves together into a torch, lit it and stuck it in the ground, and by its light quickly charged six cartridges with powder, but no shot, and stuffed the ends with dry leaves.

I loaded the gun with three rounds and fired them off at half-minute intervals. After waiting five minutes without an answer, I fired the next three. Again there was no reply. As I sat by the fire, which now gave enough light, and began to recharge the cartridges, a pistol fired somewhere. I went on loading, in case it was thought I was just someone coming across the frontier from Brazil half drunk. I fired off another three. The high Brazilian shouting came through the trees and I was sure it was Smiler and his band. I tried to imitate the peculiar note of this call until, as we drew nearer, we could hear each other distinctly.

After half an hour of walking slowly and shouting, I saw a torch, and Smiler came up, shocked at my appearance, his cheeks pouched and his lips hanging in genuine concern.

"Friend, what happened to you? Where are your Indians? And your food?"

I explained briefly that I had been washed out. He took my hand with unexpected gentleness and his brow was furrowed. "Come along, my friend. You just lie down in my camp and rest."

CHAPTER EIGHT

Brazilian Interlude

WHEN I had warmed myself at their fire and eaten, he and the other two asked me for details. As I told them my story, all Smiler would say was that I had been very lucky, very lucky. After a cup of coffee and a chip of Brazilian tobacco, I felt much better. Smiler began talking about putting me across the river in a day or two: he was thinking of his investment of stores and of getting me back to my diamond country. But I knew it would be unwise as heavier floods might come and put me in a worse position than before, so I said that it was no use and that I must stay till the end of the rains. Then he considered the realities and complained that it might be one or two months before the rains were clear. Nevertheless, I said I must stay.

"If you stay the Indians will go to your camp and take your diamonds," he warned.

"No," I lied reassuringly. "I buried them in the ground."

"Ah, that's good." He pulled out his whisky again. I took a good dram.

They slung me a dry hammock and I turned in, feeling safe in their company for the first time, for now I had nothing to lose except the little that was left of the money he had paid me, and my gun. In the morning they told me they were going to a pool in the jungle where some Brazilians had begun to dive for diamonds, which they were planning to buy, but they could not take me along, as they intended to work themselves. I said I might as well come and work too, as there was nothing I could do here. Again they tried to persuade me to return to the hills and offered me rations so that I could stay until the water went down, but eventually I persuaded them to take me.

The oxen were led off in a line and we crossed the frontier at night without a word on the march, since they had no business to be on the British side and had no intention of being discovered. After two hours they made a fire, ate and drank. I slung my hammock and slept again. We came into the savannahs during the next two days, picking our way through the sandpaper trees, as the low bushes with rough leaves are called. It was fine travelling after the dimness of the jungle. They followed their own secret line, which made a great curve into Brazilian territory and back into Guiana, to the banks of a large river. After several days we reached solid sandstone country with huge boulders in the creeks, which I saw at once must be good diamond country. In a camp by a creek we found the party—eleven men, including Brazilians, Dominicans, Portuguese and two Chinese—with huge stacks of rations, two diving helmets and a see-saw pump with a patched, bulging hose.

They gave us a noisy welcome and my troupe explained

that I had been washed out and was looking for work. I had picked up the habit of keeping quiet and said little among these strangers. A stocky fellow with a big mouth and close-cropped head, José, took charge of me. His neck had been slashed at some time with a knife, and three of his front teeth were missing, but he had a reassuring manner. He wandered about in the sun with nothing on except shorts and black rattan sandals; he must have been about forty, but he was as hard as *tasso*, the Brazilian dried meat. As everyone talked at once he asked me where I had been working and I told him high in the mountains with the Indians. He admitted that it was a good area as the diamond sources were in higher land, but insisted that it was difficult to work there unless one knew the Indians and jungle life.

Round about their camp several traders had, in the past, set up their trading huts, which are called *butus*, and I saw several derelict ones. The usual *butu* is between two trees, merely a shelter with a couple of bags of flour stacked above, some packets of cigarettes stuck in a branch and a pot boiling on the fire. The Brazilians were setting out from this customary base to dive a pool on a nearby tributary of one of the rivers. Everyone was heavily laden, so they were glad of an extra hand, and gave me one of the helmets to carry on my back. As we straggled along the trail, most of them were tipping up rum bottles and calling at the tops of their voices to each other that they would take a week's rest after the dive. They asserted that they would make at least a thousand dollars and I found them bright and invariably optimistic.

They had already been diving, and during the rest period had eaten enormous meals to replace the great amount of calories lost underwater. Two days' march brought them to the main river; they moved careless of the noise, struggling for a mile along the track, quite unlike the disciplined Indian file. They had frightened all the game for miles around, but did not care for fresh meat, relying on salted *tasso* and bought rations. It was a different life altogether. They cursed, swore and laughed and talked of who would dive first. The only quiet one was José, who, I discovered, was the foreman. Although he looked like the rest of the ruffians, he had a level head.

José owned the pump and helmets. Whoever has such equipment on the frontier can draw men to work, apparently from out of the air. One share goes to the pump, one to the rations, and the rest of the spoils are split evenly among the men. It was a pleasant change to be in open country away from heavy water and constant rain, but I was in two minds whether to try to go back over it alone, to make another attempt to reach the Indians, or to stay and work. I asked José if he thought it was possible, but he waved it aside: the rivers higher up would still be running hard despite the dryness of the country we were moving through. Almost every day I asked the same question and got the same reply, which I found comforting, as I did not want to think I was deserting the Indians, although I knew well enough that to return was impossible at present.

As soon as we reached the chosen pool I found plenty of work. Every man started cutting logs with José's axes to make rafts and a platform in the centre of the pool for the pump. We cut and hacked and dragged wood for more than a week before we were ready to dive. A ladder from the platform for the diver and dugout canoes to carry the gravel completed the equipment. The water was about twenty feet deep and diving seemed easy. The last thing was the camp, which was rushed up. Only the cook ate during the day as there was some danger of vomiting underwater on a full stomach, which, in the clumsy helmets, may mean death, as every diver knows, even at twenty feet. The only refreshment allowed, therefore, was coffee, and large cans of it were carried frequently to the platform: my job as I awaited my dive.

They started diving at six in the morning and changed every hour; my first dive was at four in the afternoon. Although it was a haphazard performance—the equipment was antiquated and the men wore no suits—the rule against eating was strictly enforced. Any man caught eating had his dive cancelled for that day, which meant losing his share of whatever he might find. But there was no restriction on drink. Most men swallowed the best part of half a bottle of rum before putting on the dented helmet with its varicosed pipe, patched here and there with insulating tape. Some were almost drunk in their effort to summon Dutch courage. José drank with them on the platform, and gave them a final swig and laugh as he clapped them under the dome.

As each man sent up his gravel, it was collected in a canoe to await him. After his dive he washed it himself, attended by José, who put the diamonds in individual kitties marked with the man's name. These were sealed and new kitties issued next day, so that eventually José had a large sack filled with kitties, each with a few diamonds.

Before my dive on the first day they had brought up over sixty carats. Soon the main talk was of the day's finds and each man described what he had found. Some stones were three carats; there were many one-carat stones, many good cleavages and some industrials. It was not a normal run, being either of very good stones or small bad ones. Altogether the haul came to around three hundred pounds sterling, so that most of the men reckoned they had made twenty pounds for themselves that day.

All this heartened me as I went out in the canoe to the waiting José. He talked quietly; told me to take everything easy and breathe normally. I must not bend my head down below my waist or the water would force its way through the padding on my chest and flood the helmet. If I was afraid or in trouble I was to give three jerks on the pipe and they would pull me up at once. There was no safety line and the men were lowered by the pipe only. If I had known anything of diving, I would never have risked my life by such crazy methods.

As I clambered awkwardly into the water, silence wrapped around me except for the pulse of the pump working up and down above. When I reached the bottom, the pressure forced the water into the helmet and I could feel it bubbling around my neck, forced down slightly at each pump stroke. I knew that if they missed one stroke above, the helmet would immediately fill. None of the Brazilians ever thought such a catastrophe could happen to him. There was at least one guarantee of life: there were no enemies in the crew. At the slightest sign of a quarrel the guilty party was to be fired. José had drummed this in, saying that he would tolerate no trouble lest it risk a life. As a result of his firmness, the crew were on good terms with each other and a camaraderie grew among us.

When I had finished my turn on the gravel I felt tugs from above and was hauled up to the ladder. After washing my gravel I found two stones of two carats and some smaller ones, so that I estimated that I had made fifteen pounds for myself that day. It was good going, but I still hankered after the hills and bigger finds that I knew I could make up there in greater safety. Most of all I missed life with the Indians, which had become idyllic. But the company was good in the camp and the days passed quickly as we worked on into July for about forty days. At the end of that time we had collected more than four hundred carats. The first day had been the best.

The pumps were stopped and the platform dismantled, for as far as they were concerned the pool was finished. But I knew they had only worked a small patch and that there remained five or six times the amount of diamonds we had removed: these crews have such a vast area to choose from that they would rather switch capriciously from pool to pool than work one thoroughly. The country is so large that a man may spend a lifetime working profitably in one place without competition or the sight of anyone.

José called us all together and after much calculation it appeared that each man would get about three hundred pounds sterling for his month's work—it was all profit, as his food was found. As I was a new man I was given a gratuity of one hundred pounds, for I did not have their skill under water and had not made the same hauls, nor had I been with them on their earlier trips. It seemed a small return, but it did not trouble me: I was quite content to have passed the time and to have enough at the end of it to make up my lost stores with a fresh lot. My sole object was to get back to the village.

I discovered that José was a smart foreman. One evening he offered me cash on the spot for my share of the diamonds and I accepted. He asked me not to tell the others. Meanwhile, each evening he produced several bottles of rum and got the crew roaring drunk: as the men staggered about in the firelight and eventually fell asleep where they lay, he opened their parcels and removed a few stones, so making up his own kitty to add to the three shares to which he was already entitled. The men never counted their stones and did not notice the change in their parcels, which had been done up with much ceremony, including grubby entries in a dog-eared notebook. After a few days roistering in the bush they sent off two men to scout for the "pirates." These returned in a day to say that the pirates were coming and that the rivers had gone down. I immediately told José I wanted to return to the Orinduik region, saying I would pay him twenty pounds if he would help me on my way. He nodded, but with his queer honesty turned down the money. Before I left I proposed to go round the camp and collect several good straw hats thrown out by the men, who, now that they had money, intended to buy shining new outfits, although many of their things were hardly worn. Even good hand-made leather shoulder bags were thrown out, and I made a fine haul, knowing these things would be appreciated by the Indians.

On the morning the buyers were expected, the men lay about eating heartily, several fires going with huge chunks of beef bubbling in the pots. Rubbish lay everywhere: empty tins, hats, shoes, matches and two drunks in a litter of bottles playing cards, fumbling and shouting or cursing according to their luck. I was lying back, recuperating from the days of work, when gunfire cracked beyond the sandpaper trees. José got up with his hands in his pockets: it was probably the buyers, so he sent a man to guide them in. In a few minutes the man came trudging back through the sand; from behind a boulder, following him, came an Indian. I was on a rise and could not see what tribe he was from. Then I recognised John.

He stood there, a little apart, looking at the crew and their rubbish. I ran down calling his name. He had an *aragebuza* in his hand and a dead bird, but he dropped both and ran towards me. He did not seem to know what to do, springing from one leg to the other and flapping his arms, breathlessly repeating:

"Yapung, me thought you lost. Me thought you lost. Indian worried plenty. All man out." He pointed in all directions.

"I am all right here," I said. "I come away from river. Everything is good now."

"Come quick. Me carry. Come quick." He wanted to get me away from the Brazilians straight away, as Indians do not usually care for their noisy expansiveness. José had come up and I told him I would like to leave at once before the meal was finished: already I was looking forward to Indian fare, which was much tastier. All I required from José was some coffee and tobacco: he went to his store and pulled out three long tobacco rolls like French bread, and an immense tin of coffee, which John put in his *warishi*. We linked arms and I tramped off through the camp, waving and calling out that I was on my way, amid roars of laughter.

"You have found your monkey brothers now. You are all right," they called. "They probably want to get you married."

In a moment we were out of sight, and soon the shouts and singing faded and we were alone. I asked John who was with him and he told me that two of the boys new to the village had come and that the others were searching near some falls in the district. They had found none of the boxes I had lost, but the sugar was still there and traces of flour; they had seen my blazing on the trees but could not trace me after I had swum through the floods and across the river. I said that if they did not know how I had done that it remained my secret. I asked about my supplies that had gone on with them and he said that they were all in good order and had been stored

139

carefully out of the rain. Everyone, he said, was waiting anxiously for news of me. I told him my plan was to go to Orinduik, buy more supplies, then trek straight on to the village, and I asked how many men were around to carry stores. About eight, he told me, but all scattered over many square miles.

They had planned a rendezvous, as they usually do, near where my riverside camp had been. When we caught up with the new boys I sent one off to bring the others from their meeting place. I told him to be at the place where we left the Brazilian traders in a day, and he nodded eagerly and ran off. I took my party nearly into Orinduik at night and under a tree found a Negro trader who spoke a little English, to whom I spun a yarn about having come from a camp nearby and wanting some stores. I bought out his little *butu*, leaving only enough for him, and spent most of the night with small scales weighing out the lot, which cost me thirty-five pounds. Two Indians piled their *warishis* high and padded off in the dark. The ground was hard and the air dry so it was good going under the moon and we made several trips during the night to the place where Smiler had left me on the original trip out of Orinduik. We sat by the stores and from four in the morning till sunrise talked incessantly, my asking for all the news in detail. Since John had seen the fancy cloth I had bought openly before him, and knew the fine load destined for the village, he was even more willing to talk. My gesture would confirm their hope that I wanted their trust and liked being with them.

Next day as I lay resting, they came running through the trees shouting my name, and shook my hammock, joking about my disappearance.

"River take you over Old Man Falls maybe."

"Tiger take you."

"You climb tree and go into sky." And so on it went in high excited tones with laughter.

"Oh, Yapung," said Labba, as he came up last, "all women *kalewi, kalewi*—all the women cry for you." This was, of course, a nice sentiment rather than literal truth.

No orders were needed, and they quickly ended their greetings, packed the *warishis* and stood waiting with bended heads and straining straps. I got out of my hammock.

"This time I punish like Indian," I said, in explanation of my experiences.

"Ah, you *kapung*. You Indian. You no punish," they laughed.

So we set out for the village.

CHAPTER NINE
The Sandhills

THE way back was strange: all had been changed by the rains.
Renewed in strength the jungle had blossomed; we cut our way
through green shoots, in some places having to diverge half
a mile—nothing in open country but a major task in the thick
forest. The leaves brought down by the high winds and the
incessant rains had formed a thick slushy carpet over which
the Indians spread their toes, clawing their way up the slopes.
My rubber boots were useless and I copied them, for even on
rubble the Indians' grip was surer than any boot, and I saw

that in comparison to their feet mine were like atrophied stumps.

The creeks were changed, too: where there had been a straight stretch was now a bend cut under raw, falling earth; where there had been the edge of a small parched plateau was now an eroded hump, dissolved under the scour of a muddy waterfall. Rapids had been formed here, bare rock exposed there. Drifting trees had formed sandbanks; old ones had gone; great trees, standing as landmarks for years, had vanished, and everywhere there was the feeling of dissolution and renewal. Without a compass, I relied entirely on the Indians, who found their way by signs and a sense of direction too subtle for me to grasp. Even when they went a mile off course they came back unerringly on trail.

The village had not escaped either and half the cassava crop was lying on the ground, uprooted—a serious loss. The Indians would have to reap the crop whether the shoots were ripe or not, and replanting would be an additional task that year. Beyond the flattened fields I looked for signs of welcome. They were all there waiting for me, standing in a row with the tallest at one end, tailing to the shortest at the other. A small boy finding himself between two men looked up on either side and moved down the line to find someone of his own size to talk with. There they stood on the hill and waited, some smiling, none showing excitement, and I found this quietness more impressive than a noisy welcome.

As soon as the men passed among them everyone began to discuss my adventures and the Brazilians. They were interested in everything, although the women frowned at the mention of my recent hosts: they had little liking for them— a natural conservatism, perhaps, shown by most women when confronted with people of another race. The men, on the other hand, were not so ungenerous: no doubt they recalled the good wages one or two of them had been paid when they had worked with prospectors.

I reviewed my position and reckoned that so far my expedition had been a business failure: I had lost my supplies and made them up again, but at great expense of time. The villagers had one simple view of it all. I had produced supplies before, so I would do so again. Fortunately I was able to bring back more than they had expected, and I decided to gamble on liberality and to hand out plenty for all.

First I rested for a day or two, getting my hut into shape. Some of the thatching needed repair but fortunately most things were in order. No one had visited my farm while I was away, although the rain had been so violent that the villagers had been hard pressed to find food for themselves. Hunting had been impossible and they had relied on fishing and the big reserves of cassava bread and cassili which they keep. Any small birds in range of blowpipes had been fair game to vary the daily bread and fish. So when I arrived with my stores I was doubly welcome, as they were at the last of their food: everyone took a large ration of flour, sugar and salt; the women took cloth; to the children I gave strips of cloth for *saloes*. However, I gave the men no powder and shot: I intended to dole out these vital stores slowly.

When I reached the farm I saw great changes. Many of the plants were down. Worst of all, the banana plants had been uprooted by floods pouring down the slope. So many of the surrounding trees had fallen that I was able to plant an extra half-acre without felling any timber, putting the new plants in between the fallen trunks, with the minimum of work. Later, when the sun had dried the trunks I intended to burn them.

When I went to the creek by the sag where I had struck diamonds, I found the water deep owing to stoppages of branches and leaves, and so I took a party down and cleared the rubbish out; but knowing I had diamonds there for the taking I did no more. In any case the villagers were busy themselves repairing their farms and progress on all fronts was slow. I helped them to plant their fields as I knew they could do nothing without being certain of their own food. All this took time and it was a month before we could draw breath and look ahead.

I was sure we had seen all the real rain for the year, having had such severe floods. Before me I saw a clear run of serious prospecting and I planned to range far afield. It so happened that the Indians furthered this idea around the village fires.

I had caught the Indian habit of drinking cassili and could not do without it, most evenings sitting with them sipping from my bowl round the fires. One evening we gathered in this way, and as usual I steered the conversation to the mountains, waterfalls and hunting trails they knew. Soon all of us were talking at once, and the two boys new to the village spoke up. They knew, they said, of a range of sandhills at the foot of a mountain, which they had approached from their own village, so that they were not sure of its distance from this village, though they thought it was about three days' away. Through the hills ran pure bluish water and coarse gravel showed clearly through it. I had never heard of a place more promising of diamonds.

I asked if there was much jungle, and they told me it was fairly open, broken country with much ironstone, which made it sound like a hill formed by an ironstone outcrop breaking through a sandstone reef. Nothing could be better for almond-pebbled gravel, which is the ideal diamond bearer. I knew that I must make a decision while they were still excited by their thoughts of the place, and so I said we would go to the hills without delay, picking for my party Peta and John as well as the two boys. Peta had proved himself a tough youngster when he had fallen out of the canoe during our trip to the fishing grounds; John was the "civilised" one and had some idea of prospecting. But I did not intend to keep all of them once I had settled in the hills, as they wanted to come back and do more work on their farms. The village was short of meat, too, they said, and they would have to be out hunting. However, there was a middle-aged widower in the village who seemed to be at a loose end.

This man seldom spoke much. His skin was unusually wrinkled for his age and his feet were a mass of lumps and scars, so I imagined he had once been a reckless hunter who had dashed over rocks without care for his skin. Sometimes Indians show off in this way when young and return from hunts with bleeding feet, despite the thick pads on their soles. This man had wandered near the frontier and had been employed for a time by an American named Isaac. On the few occasions when the old hunter talked it was of the days he had spent with "Misterisaac." Eventually the villagers forgot his real name and he became Misterisaac. Misterisaac had a maniac streak in him, which explained his once youthful recklessness and his hero worship. In fact, he had become something of a joke in the village, although it was in all seriousness that he had been nicknamed.

The boys told me that Misterisaac knew the sandhills, and I hoped he would know the trail from this village. I remarked that he lazed about a good deal and seemed to have little to do. The boys agreed, and were sure that if I said the word Misterisaac would go with me. As I knew him only slightly I felt I should prime him with a gift of some kind, so I sent the two boys for him and went back to my hut and lit the lamp. Presently I smelt him approaching. He was deliberately walking quietly and slowly to surprise me: nothing pleases an Indian more than to appear suddenly as if out of the blue, as this shows his skill and puts the other off his balance. Then he will grin from ear to ear. Misterisaac evidently intended to keep in character as a mystery brave. He came through the door and I was aware of his standing behind me, waiting for his big moment, but I did not turn round.

"*Ela-benai?* How are you?" I said brusquely.

"*Wakay be-molouuuu*—Oh, all right," he croaked slowly, as if ailing.

I turned round and produced two bakes out of a bag in my hammock. At once his voice was restored. I began to explain my plan and took down my gun, which I started to clean. Then I picked up a few flasks of powder and threw them on the table without a glance. A bag of shot followed.

"Do you know the sandhills?" I asked.

146

"Yes, me know. Me know," he replied to the powder and shot on the table.

"You take me there?"

"Now, we go now?" he said, preparing to go.

"Are you mad? It is dark. It is time to sleep."

His stare at the powder did not shift.

"All right. All right. Soon morning me come—me bring me gun. Me bring me gun."

We talked on for a few moments and at the end of each reply he continued to mention his gun.

The next morning very early Misterisaac appeared with his *aragebuza* and asked for some oil to clean it. I said that I would not only give him that but I would also give him some ammunition so that he could see that it was working well. He laughed with so much excitement that the ball of *coue-ga* he was chewing fell out of his mouth. Carelessly he turned it into the sand with his big toe, as a man might stub out a half-finished cigar.

I dipped into my bag and gave him a quarter of a flask of powder and a handful of shot, which he took quickly and carried to his house, where he sat down outside with his possessions. The other villagers came and asked him how he got it, but he looked through them and disdained to utter more than "Mmm mmm," as if a man of substance, abstracted from their idle chatter. Finally he loaded his gun as rapidly as dignity allowed and began to fire off into the air, one shot after the other. I thought from where I stood that he might well ruin the gun from the punishment he was giving it. I ran down.

"All right," I said, "gun good. You keep him quiet."

He grinned, and I told him to pack and be ready to go. It was clear that Misterisaac would not be as level-headed as Amou, but I found his antics likeable.

Towards the end of the evening I asked the women to bring me the horn and blew three blasts to call in the hunters. An hour later Peta and the two boys came in. John was still out, and I imagined that he was on the trail of game which he thought worth pursuing farther. I told the others that Misterisaac had agreed to come and that my plans were made: we would move out to the hills as rapidly as possible to make a quick prospection, taking only light stores. I would keep two men while the others returned, Misterisaac and Peta. The others started coming in with one or two maams, powice and bush turkeys. The maams, which resemble large chickens with red combs like turkeys, were at their best at this season.

We had no fresh cassava cakes and had to take some that were already mouldy, but they remained quite edible even when they turned blue. I packed also plenty of flour, sugar and salt, and as we were short of meat took some tins of corned beef, one of the few tinned foods that is a useful standby in the jungle. There was some old dried cod which I intended to boil with cassava or ground yams to form a kind of strongly flavoured and palatable soup. By now I was walking on bare feet most of the time. I was as good as the Indians so long as the ground was dry, but my soles were not yet hard enough to stand damp, and were softened and stung with cuts when it rained, and I found that wearing shoes frequently seemed to prevent them hardening properly.

Peta, the two boys, John and Misterisaac were all fully laden, when we left, despite my attempts to keep stores to the minimum. As well as food we carried shovels, sieves and a tarpaulin for prospection. Instead of going down through the farms we struck out at the back of the village, cutting our way into the jungle on Misterisaac's directions. Toward the end of the first day I concluded that from what the boys had told me he was taking a long route. I could still see the mountains above the village, so I asked him if he was keeping straight towards the sandhills: he reassured me, apparently without a thought. As the boys did not know the approach route from this point, they could not be sure that he was wrong, but I said that after two days we must surely get beyond the mountains ahead.

"No. Farther," he stated.

I put it to the boys at once, and we agreed that Misterisaac's line must take us for a four- or five-day march. We walked on, but by the end of the second day he himself began to be worried and confused, which was so unusual for an Indian that at first I could hardly believe that he might be right off the correct course. He had said that we should have come to a big creek where we could camp that evening, but we met no creek, so I sent him on with Peta and John to look for it. I stayed back with the two boys and had a serious discussion with them. Then I told them to go off, one on each side, and that they must find the creek, now before the sun went down. I gave one my gun and they dropped their packs and ran off, the other with his bow and arrows, while I stayed where I was to await results.

Within twenty minutes one returned.

"We are walking away from the creek," he said.

He had found it by going back down the trail and making a cross cut through the jungle. The creek was not running hard and the fluttering of the leaves and other jungle noises had prevented us from hearing it. I told him to pick up his *warishi* and cut a trail to the creek to await the rest of us. I estimated that Misterisaac's trail would eventually have brought us out in the right area but by a much longer route than necessary. When the other boy came back I went with him to the creek and blew three blasts with the gun to call the others. When Misterisaac arrived I asked him if he was leading us a dance to punish us.

"You *amako* now—you old man now. Your head is soft," I told him. He smiled.

"Me know. Mountain that way. We go this way." He waved his arm at his old track.

"All right. We follow this creek. We know it comes from the mountains and we get there quicker."

He was satisfied that we had found the right creek and we camped, but he spent the rest of the evening convincing the others that he would have got there eventually. This was necessary for him as, like all Indians, the others would not have tolerated being led on a wild-goose chase by a bad guide.

149

For hours we lay awake, plagued by sandflies, which the fire was unable to keep off. How I wished that I had a mosquito net with me! Then I remembered a small bottle of kerosene, undressed, and rubbed it all over myself. It worked, but I could hear the Indians continuing to slap at intervals, cursing softly. We should never have camped on a sandy patch so close to water, and we set out tired the next day.

The trail rose through very thick jungle, and all day we swung our knives against endless creepers and branches, clambering over boulders and up steep slopes. One man cut a pilot trail ahead; the rest of us cut to get our *warishis* through. We blazed the trees heavily with slashes on one side to show the way we were going: on large trees the Indians stripped the bark for a yard and cut a deep X with one or two deft strokes. This mark on the injured bark would not heal.

We kept a sharp look-out for any traces of man but could see none, not even the temporary camps to be found in hunted jungle, so I thought it probable that we were going through jungle never explored before. Vast tracks of uninhabited jungle exist and this seemed to be one. On the third day we fired at one or two acouris, animals resembling hares, and roasted them with pleasure. Then we began to discover many fruits, including peaches, whose exceptionally powerful scent was discernible at a hundred yards. They were small, but very juicy and sweet. We also found large wild cocoa pods, broke the branches, brought them down, and split their skins to drink the juices and eat the tender, jelly-like beans. I noticed the chigga-knit fruit, which the Indians did not know—a whitish fruit with brown spots about an inch in diameter resembling the full-grown jigger, which infests human feet. The Indians then showed me a fruit I had never seen before, which tasted, they said, like jamoun, a small blackberry. The fruit was in hard yellow walnut-shaped pods on a tree about five feet high: in the pods was a black paste like boot polish with a few tiny seeds like the simatou. Both the paste and the seeds were sweet and pleasant to eat and the Indians naturally liked it, as they have sweet tooths. There were many other fruits and the hunting was good, and I wondered why the Indians had never made a settlement on this higher and more bountiful region.

On reflection, I realised that there were three objections: the creek was not navigable, it probably dried up between the rains, and there would be no fish. Without plenty of water it would be useless. We filled ourselves with the fruits as we went along, but at the end of the third day we had not reached the sandhills. At twilight they pointed out a steep ridge ahead which showed through the thinning trees. We had to make our way over a pass it seemed: then we would be in sight of the hills.

At camp that night I urged them to eat as much cassava bread as possible to lighten the packs for the mountain trip next day and we laid into the corned beef as well. With such good hunting country and plenty of fruit I was not worried about shortage of food.

Next morning, the fourth day, we washed in the creek early, changed straps on the *warishis* and made all shipshape for the trip. For an hour we continued climbing along the general course of the creek and found many tributaries, some of them deep. I decided that we must be careful here to make a clear trail across them, as we did not relish swimming in the still black water with no idea of what lay beneath—although there would be no electric eels so high in the hills, there might have been other unknown dangers. After going some distance we found an old corkwood tree lying across a creek. One man dropped his pack and reached the other side; another followed with his *warishi*. As he reached the centre I could see the bark sinking under the weight of his feet and the tree began bending, so I called him back. We made a small raft and pulled the packs across while we went singly over the tree. As we pushed on, the flies came again and all of us were badly bitten and covered with red bumps: it is unusual for sandflies to bite in broad daylight and I supposed that we were reaching a height where their food—warm-blooded animals

151

—was scarce. The worst stage was after the march, when the blood ceased circulating rapidly and itching began, so much that we tore our skins with scratching.

As we rose towards the pass, the climbing became dangerous, over much loose sandstone which dropped away for hundreds of feet. We made slow progress and eventually reached the crossing of the spur. From the ridge I looked down. Below me were the sandhills, cut by numerous watercourses, as the boys had described, lying in a vast hidden basin. Their silent barrenness and the glitter of the water for many miles seemed promising, so I decided to camp on the ridge for the night and reach the sandhills, where we would unload, on the morrow, the fifth day. The party would then return to the village, leaving myself, Peta and Misterisaac. I told them they must take their time on the return journey, which was to be cut as directly to the village as possible and well-blazed.

I was still uneasy about keeping Misterisaac with me, but as I had told the others they could return to work at home, it seemed wrong to alter my decision at this stage. I told them to wait for the coming moon and also for the next one and then return to call me by the horn if I had not come back to the village. This arrangement allowed me about six weeks in the hills.

Before they went they helped look for a suitable base camp. I decided after a while that we should camp on high ground where there would be a good view of the sandhills. We chose a high bare ridge above a creek about thirty feet wide which, judging by the movement of the water and the type of trees at the banks, was exceptionally deep, and built a strong shelter of wood and palm leaves, big enough for all the stores and three hammocks. We slung the stores from the beams, set up the hammocks, and sat about in the sand cleaning our guns and talking, while the boys gathered wood for our fire. They put up barbecues for the salted meat, which was now weevily, and the remains of the fish, soft and becoming rotten, was put over the fire, and the cassava bread slung on the rafters. I was glad to see that the flies seemed scarcer, but I was vaguely troubled by the amount of water that poured through the many gullies around us and in the big creek below, which seemed an exceptional flow for the time of year. I felt that the best spots in the area would be higher up at the source of the creeks, from where the diamonds would be carried. But we were on a spur at the back of which there was no natural route of escape. These points occurred to me but not to the Indians, who feel safe in most places, as they rarely anticipate staying anywhere for long except in their villages.

The other problem was the old man who, I was certain, hoped, having brought me to the sandhills, to laze his time away. He had his gun and ammunition which would be enough for him, and I was worried by the thought that he might wander off with it and not find his way back to me. However, as the boys would have cut the trail out I would not be lost.

As we were in new country and high up, I intended to make the camp as safe as possible from strange animals, particularly the tigers and jaguars of the hills, many of whose trails I had noticed. I put the old man to work cleaning the brushwood around the shelter for about twenty yards, and behind the camp at some distance we dug a rubbish pit to keep away ants and snakes, as we had noticed many anthills, particularly of the drogher ants. Should they reach a camp, they make the trail up to it, wait till night and then move in, slitting the bags of food to carry each grain away, removing all by daylight. They do not climb into camp shelters, and it is wise to sling all food above ground. I hoped that if any should attack, it would be on the garbage pit. Peta agreed that it would be best to put our fires well beyond the shelter, so that we could see the perimeter of the clearing, as a protection against tigers and snakes.

In the following days the three of us, Peta, the old man, and myself, started prospecting, each taking a shovel and going to different areas. I sent the other two to probe the lower stretches of the creeks, while I wandered where I fancied with my sieves. When the sun rose to noon each day we returned to eat at the camp. Whenever I sieved that first day I found many indications of diamonds—mica, quartz and other minerals —but no diamonds. I called the others and told them I thought the area was difficult to work. The stones indicating the presence of diamonds were not widely scattered and I said we would make cross-cuts on a chosen creek by digging on one side, moving down ten feet and probing on the other.

"If we dig one small pit, another pit on one creek—one moon pass quick," said Peta.

I agreed, and decided to limit each creek to six test pits so that we could cover a wide area. Peta was satisfied and we started work, each man digging one pit. It required no thought but much hard work, as the sand was damp and mixed with clay and did not fall into the pits. But the gravel was deep in most places.

Sometimes we struck gravel at four feet, at other points we came to clay at once. Soon we had a good idea of the drift of the gravel strata. From each of the six pits dug on the first day were collected several buckets of gravel for me to wash. Next day while the others started on another creek I washed the gravel at each pit and found nothing, although the indications were strong everywhere. I knew that with the indications I was getting in this type of country that there must be diamonds somewhere. I had an inspiration, and dropping my sieve, I ran to the camp for my batel and mercury vial.

The batel is a shallow cone-shaped pan used for tracing the finest particles of gold or the smallest stones. Once back at the creek I started with the batel on all the old gravel I had discarded. I threw two shovel loads in the batel with a dash of mercury. Now, I thought, if anything is passing through my sieves I will find out what it is. I shook the batel just above the water in the creek, dipped it and gave it a shake so that the larger grains swirled to the surface. I shook it again and scraped the top layer off. I kept on doing this until most of the gravel was out and any heavy minerals had sunk, I hoped, to the timbal, which is the bottom of the cone.

Then I began to spin the batel with the deft twist that comes with practice, dipping it in the water, so that the remaining sand swung out in a fan across the batel and out at the edge. When I had nearly come in sight of the mercury I stirred the contents of the timbal. I spun some more sand out and drained most of the water. I shook the batel for the last time and tilted it towards me quickly. The water ran out, the sand strung itself in a line towards my eye and I tapped the batel to make the grains jump onwards towards the edge. In the final streak all the mineral traces arranged themselves in order of their specific gravity.

But there was nothing in the first batel. I tried the second pit and found very fine gold bearings. This was what I had suspected: the minute grains were slipping through my sieves. I collected altogether about ten "eyes," the technical name for spots of gold, which was a fair indication, considering other factors. Then I went to the pit Peta was digging. I bateled there and when I had come to the last spin I found four tiny diamonds —"sands"—which would run about a hundred to the carat. I refrained from calling to the others lest it break the system of their work. Instead, I told them quietly not to dig deep in new pits as I only wanted enough gravel at each to fill a batel.

When I got to the camp I took the mercury which had attached itself to the gold, dropped it in a handkerchief and squeezed it. The mercury ran out, leaving the gold. I put the gold on the tip of a shovel over the fire and evaporated the remains of the mercury. The gold melted together in a little blob. It was too much work to be worth while but useful as an indication for diamonds. The diamonds, too, were a good indication but too small to work for their own sake and I felt that I must get higher up the creeks nearer their sources. Meanwhile for several days I continued to batel and to find small diamonds until we decided to look in higher ground on short trips from the base camp.

In the second week we travelled up the creeks to their sources and found the same indications as before but many times larger. The pieces of carbon and mica were twenty or thirty times the weight of the pieces below but still there were no diamonds. I told Peta and Misterisaac that I had found strong indications including gold. They were very pleased as it meant that we were not wasting time.

"Diamond *yapung* big, very big," I said, "but no diamond."

Peta thought. "Sometime," he said slowly, "diamond *yapung* come bottom side, diamond stay topside. Diamond heavy."

It seemed sound reasoning. He pointed higher up the mountain.

"Plenty waterfall. Diamond catch there. *Yapung* come down here."

We went higher and stayed another week in the mountain. Again the maddening indications, stronger than ever, but no diamonds worth sieving. I found only one stone worthy of the name, a pretty, half-carat diamond. We had shifted sandstone boulders before finding it and I was sure that although a fortune lay there, it was bottled up in the line of the waterfalls amid the sandstone reefs.

CHAPTER TEN

Trapped

W᙮ came back to our main camp in despondency, the first we had shown among ourselves. No one spoke, and Mister-isaac got down wearily on to his thin, muddy haunches and began puffing life into the fire to cook, managing an occasional grin, with the inevitable piece of cassava bread in his mouth. We turned in early, but the night passed slowly, as I lay thinking of where next I might try and listening to the rustle of every leaf as they dropped through the unusually dry air and blew along the sand. The whole jungle was dry and there was a constant crackling as if the trees were stretching themselves. Misterisaac sat against the post by the fire scratching fitfully, first under his arm, then on his stomach. He had probably got an itch from brushing a plant resembling the edoe, which acts like a nettle and grows near creeks or swamps: I felt slightly irritated and suggested that he should take a bath. He declined, saying that he had only one *saloe* with him.

As we talked on, we became aware of a noise up by the falls behind us. Short, soft whines warned us of a jaguar beginning his growl and suddenly along the mountainside there was a crashing as if some heavy beast were floundering through the jungle, or perhaps two animals were fighting. The growling ceased as Misterisaac confirmed that it was probably a big mountain jaguar. They are found either fawn or with spotted stripes, but both kinds grow bigger in the hills and demand more caution than those lower down.

Now the jaguar growled in full throat between heavy dragging noises. I told Misterisaac to douse the fire and take the meat out of the pot as I was unsure of the habits of these beasts and did not want to attract it. I slid from my hammock and covered the embers with sand and Misterisaac ran out of the camp and covered the pot with banana leaves to prevent the smell escaping. Peta was walking slowly into the darkness and I whistled softly to him. He whispered back that he was going down to the creek where the canyon walls would carry the sounds to him more clearly. I fetched my gun and told Misterisaac to clear out of the camp with me. The Indians told me that there had been no need to pit out the fire as no mountain jaguar would have approached it, but I could not be sure what the jaguar was up to and wanted to be in cover with the camp site as a clear field for my gun.

We stooped in the bushes and listened intently to the noises of what was now obviously a fight, the roaring and tumbling increasing in violence and continuing for nearly five minutes, when it tailed off. The jaguar gave one or two apparently triumphant snarls which echoed round the hills, and was then silent. Misterisaac clutched his *pibung*, obviously scared: I sympathised with him, as his old gun would have been less use for quick-fire than a stout bow and a handful of big-game arrows. We sat for hours, not daring to move without knowing where the jaguar had got to, and I have no doubt that on their own the Indians would have acted more efficiently. I called Peta and asked him to make a fire for which we gathered twigs from around us, but the matches were in the camp. Either of the Indians would have willingly gone for them, but I would not allow the risk. Peta then produced his flint, normally carried in a jaguar-skin bag slung by the waist from the shoulder, and struck it with the back of his hunting-knife so that the sparks streamed into a tiny bundle of leaves and the fire soon blazed. Peta and I stood up to look around, while Misterisaac remained crouching, peering in all directions and scratching.

We went back to the camp and started the main fire also, keeping both in for the few remaining hours till day, but we heard nothing. I drifted off to sleep, after deciding with the other two to go up and examine the scene of the fight for tracks. When I woke, the fire still burned and the cooking-pot was over it but there was no sign of Misterisaac, and Peta did not know where he had gone. We looked about for his tracks and saw them leading off past the rubbish heap. Peta whistled phonetically for him to return at once, but there was no answer: probably the old fellow had gone off searching on his own, I thought. Sure enough, when we had climbed the hill we heard him whistling us, saying he had found a tapir. We plunged through the undergrowth to where he stood to find a large beast torn at the neck, from which, carefully avoiding the wounded flesh, Misterisaac was cutting steaks from the hind-quarters, which he said would be good eating. He left off to join us in a search for the jaguar's tracks, as I felt that unless we found out the intention of the jaguar and its line of movement, we would be unable to work without constantly looking over our shoulders. To the Indians an occurrence like this ultimately would have been no problem. Whenever a jaguar begins to frequent the outskirts of their village, they work their way

159

close to it and give a peculiar shout which, oddly enough, frightens the jaguar away and avoids the risk of trying to kill it. The problem of a big cat in jungle is entirely different to one in open country, as favourable places in which to open fire are few: this place was not one of them.

We decided, nevertheless, to build a *wabini* over the kill and chose some rocks and a tree as the base. It was in such a position that if the wind shifted it would not carry our scent directly up his tracks into the mountain, down which we presumed he would return. They washed the sweat from their feet, then cut the branches for the *wabini* fifty yards away from the spot and built it into a fork in the tree with a support on the rock, taking care during its erection to avoid breaking any sappy leaf or twig. We got into position, one above the other, on the platforms and waited. Hours later, it seemed, when the sun was at its hottest at about two in the afternoon, the jaguar appeared.

He was the largest I had seen, with an unusually thick, sleek coat of fawn, his muscles rippling slickly as he peered about him low on the ground, far below us, as Peta had anticipated. When Misterisaac began to manœuvre his long *pibung*, with unusual clumsiness for a seasoned hunter, Peta's broad foot appeared past my shoulder and clipped Misterisaac's hand in his splayed toes. Meanwhile, the jaguar walked round the tapir sniffing and growling, finally moving away to sniff the bushes, so that we began to think he might have caught our scent. We were too far from him and not in a good position to fire: boulders lay everywhere, among which the target disappeared frequently and, if wounded, he could easily have vanished before another shot could be fired. To descend then, and fight him among this cover, was a risk we did not relish taking.

The jaguar came back, licked the tapir and began pulling flesh from the neck. Soon he was ripping and gobbling greedily. Finally, he began padding away, and I was about to descend when Peta warned us that he would be sure to return after a short look around. Sure enough, in a few minutes he was back.

He gripped the four-hundred-pound tapir by the neck, half lifted it, apparently without difficulty, and began dragging it backwards up the slope, finally disappearing with it. After a while we descended and Peta began to urge with determination that we go after him and kill him, as he would only cause plenty of trouble if we did not: he himself would go there and then with his bow. I said that if there was a slip we would not be able to correct it, nodding sideways to show that our problem was Misterisaac, who would need as much watching as the jaguar. We could, of course, have scared the jaguar away with the Indian yell: but in this case there was his kill to attract him back again. An arrow shot would be less effective among the rocks than in open country as, should he make a run, the arrow would quickly be snapped off instead of working in the wound. Peta agreed, but remained keen to take the risk.

Finally I gave in and we put ourselves under his orders. Misterisaac was persuaded to remain behind, and we set off slowly, Peta having refused my gun, saying he could swing his bow and take aim with it more quickly. We worked our way through the rocks, inch by inch, as the jaguar could not be far off with the tapir. Peta kept holding his head up to smell and listen, motioning me back to a distance so that I was unable to see clearly ahead of him. Finally we came between two rocks standing with flat faces towards each other; here Peta froze. As if in slow motion, his bow rose smoothly and his taut arm hauled back the heavy iron-tipped arrow to his ear. He held the position for several seconds, then suddenly swung sideways, bending his right knee to see round the rock and released the arrow.

The end was an anticlimax. There was one roaring snarl as Peta swung back; I brought my gun to cover his open side and heard the thumps as the jaguar leapt around. Then the noise quickly sank to a bubbling rumble. We heard threshing and beating but the jaguar did not run, and I knew he must be fatally hit. Again Peta sent an arrow round the rock. When we eventually came out of cover, the explanation was clear: Peta's first arrow had driven almost three-quarters of its six foot length straight under the left shoulder from behind and slightly obliquely from above, striking true into his heart and emerging the other side. The second had caught him in the bowels and seized him stationary in the death agony. I have rarely seen such daring and deadly fire from a bow. After we had whistled, Misterisaac came up in great excitement, and out came his knife at once to begin skinning the beast. But Peta had lost interest, and we gave it up to go home and cook a meal of tapir steak. For days afterwards we were reminded of the kill by occasional wafts of the smell of rotting flesh.

Further prospecting showed perfect indications of fairly heavy diamond deposits in the surrounding creeks: we even kept finding fine diamonds, the surest signs of all. All I could do was to cut my boundary lines for a claim, and on this task we spent the next week. I made out my forms to send to the Lands and Mines Office, although I had no means of dispatching them.

I reviewed my position. We had scoured the sandhills and we had been into the mountains, but in neither area had diamonds been within the reach of my meagre resources. I reasoned this way: higher up we had dug down to sandstone and lower down the slope we had come to clay; further down still I had touched sandstone again. The clay was only a bluff, and I knew from experience that very often the sandstone strata beyond and below a strip of clay is the richest ground of all. I washed a piece of the clay and found as many indications in it as I had in any gravel. That confirmed my surmise, and I decided to make camp below the spur we had first crossed, where I would batel the sandstone strata where it rose out of the clay.

The new camp was in a fine place on a rocky outcrop clear of all but a few trees, and seemed a spacious, airy platform from which to view our new ground. Standing there, we could see a creek circle round below, and above the mountain spur rose to block any retreat. I sat and looked at the maze of creeks below, where the lazy waters, sparkling in bends among the sands, lost their perspective somehow and took on an *Alice in Wonderland* disproportion. To my pork-knocker's eye there was something wrong in this too-neat land-scape. Sand lay heaped and smoothed where there should have been no sand. The creek banks were smoothed as if wet hands had moulded them in clay. It was all too clean and bare.

I forgot my uneasiness; it might, I thought, have been caused by the sun reflecting on many slivers of water, and, leaving the men to cut the lines, I went down and squatted by a creek. My batel showed indications, fewer than before but larger. I moved down a few hundred yards and bateled. Just as I had finished the first washing, I heard a noise in the water higher up which might have been a stone rolling into the stream. I looked back at the batel. In it was the dream of pork-knockers—"brown eyes," flat grey or light brown stones the size of halfpennies, huge "tins" or broken graphite; many round, smooth water-worn carbons, so big they banged in the batel as I swung it round; micas; and a small stone like quartz, only a pretty blue. There were diamonds here, sure enough, but it would mean months of work to get them out. I wanted money at once and thought of my modest little sag which, although poor compared to this brazen, sunny, sinister landscape, would give me a few hundred dollars at any time I dug in it. As I thought and stirred the micas, tins and brown eyes, something recalled the odd noise. Moving my head slightly, I glanced over my shoulder: I could see the tips of an Indian's toes.

It was the first time an Indian had managed to creep up on me: the clean smell of creek water and the sight of my batel had spoiled my nose and sense. I knew from the short, stubbed toes alone that it was Misterisaac, and turning, I asked him what he wanted.

"O, I don't know," he groaned, looking at the sky as if nothing was out of the ordinary.

"Are the lines finished?"

"Me finish. Me finish. Me come now. Me hungry."

"All right, go in the camp and eat something."

"You find? You find?" he asked suddenly brightening.

"No," I said, anticipating the next question. I thumped the edge of the batel with my thumb so that it sank a little in the water and the indications were swept about in the miniature turmoil.

"Indications? Me see. Me see."

If it had been Peta or any of the others, I would have shown all that was there, but Misterisaac was too strange and I did not like being surprised.

"I spin it out," I said, and washed out most of the heavy stuff, leaving only a few fine tins amid the sand.

"You look," I said, "and see. Very good. Good." I told him.

"This good?"

"Yes," I assured him.

If he became interested in such small indications as now lay in my batel, he might at least tell me when he found similar signs on his own. I knew from his face that he took my words seriously and I felt that I had made the right impression on the old man. I told him to go and cook something for us; we would whistle Peta in from his hard work cutting the lines of the claims.

The lines have to be about four or five feet wide and straight, so that a surveyor's chain can be dragged evenly through them and so that each stage can be seen clearly from one location board to the next. But I did not cut my lines down to the ground, intending that by the next dry season they would again be overgrown: this was my method of preventing their easy discovery by claim jumpers, for when alone, as I was, one needed cunning to protect one's interests.

After Misterisaac left for the camp, I sat for some time by the creek with the batel in my hand. I knew now that I had found a rich region, a real El Dorado. I thought of all the places I had searched in—they covered a wide area and it was clear that diamonds were scattered in patches over it. It seemed unbelievable that the diamonds could have been so swept across spurs, over sandhills, and through streams, as though a god had sprinkled giant handfuls here and there about the land-

164

scape. It takes time—perhaps ten years—to find a pocket of diamonds, but when discovery comes it is at least of a modest fortune for a man who is prepared to work. As I thought like this, I felt tired. I gazed at the acres of what could be my fortune: the immensity of it was overwhelming, and the prospect sated the imagination. I could want no more. But of course it was all in the ground; it was not there to spend. Yet always in the years ahead I would remember this spot as the one where I could come for wealth. The thought was comforting as well as drugging: the discovery was sufficient to sap the incentive to work. All I wanted was to lie down there and sleep like Rip Van Winkle.

This I knew to be the genuine attitude of the pork-knocker, as opposed to that of the clear-headed man who comes in, makes his find and gets out. For the old pork-knocker the life becomes a dream and an intention to mine diamonds in the future, but never in the present. Those whom the younger pork-knockers respect are known for their knowledge of the diamond lands but not for their wealth. These old men often ask for a meal, and if they are asked where there are rich lands they will say, "You see that hill. Well, I've walked all those places, prospected them, dug all those creeks; good indications!" Asked why they have not worked, they will have no reply, but in the silence is the implication that they could not have ranged so far and wide if they had stuck in one spot and worked. To make them happy and proud, it is only necessary to invite them to talk of the things they have done and the places they have known. But do not ask them what money they have made out of it.

No doubt, behind their curious reluctance to cash in is the feeling that I now had. I felt that I was in a country of minerals where I could make a find whenever I chose. The sensation was a novel one in a world generally driven by desire and want, and I was filled with the reverse impulse: my security removed want, without actually assuaging it.

To the pork-knocker it is sufficient to be alive and to be free. If he is lucky and picks up, say, ten or fifteen thousand dollars' worth of stones, the money goes in a snap of the fingers.

It is nothing to splash this amount on a two-weeks' spree, with his wife loaded with fine clothes and rings and he himself happily drunk from morning to night. Men are living on the edge of the Pakaraima ranges with just this philosophy. It is not that they could not make money and tear themselves away. They just will not go.

The old ones may be wise in their way, for to make money there consistently is not easy. It is like roulette, with perhaps a big strike at first and then years of search to find another place, by which time the money from the first find has gone; some would say as an investment in the prospection of the lands. The greatest decision to make is to get out while the going is good. As it is in most games of chance, the odds of human nature are weighed against such restraint: few men can step aside when they have filled their pockets with diamonds for the first time. Men coming in from the outside, from French Guiana or the islands of the West Indies, have more sense than those who live in the hills. They spend a few years there, save money all the time and go back with a fat bank account. Curiously enough, I have never heard of men going out from these diamond lands to French or Dutch Guiana to do the same thing, although huge areas in those countries lie virgin.

Some of the pork-knockers have their wives up in the diamond lands with them and they are the steady ones, the wife wielding the pick as heartily as the man and working the same creek with him, month after month. In some crews, too, there is a steady man among them. He is entrusted with the funds and makes the trek to the nearest post office to send money to the homes of his mates, so that they can get drunk with a clear conscience. Christmas is the one time when nearly all pork-knockers make a supreme effort to clear out for home with something in their pockets and before Christmas men will cheat and steal, even from their best friends, to scrape something together to show that they have not entirely wasted their time. For a pork-knocker to go home without a cent he must have a mean courage for, by so doing, he breaks one of the unwritten laws of his life.

I was a little abstracted as I climbed back to the camp where Peta was lying in his hammock exhausted after a day's unceasing cutting of the lines. It had been unusually hard work even for him, and I imagined that he may have been hoping for the return of the other villagers to carry out our kit—they were due in another week. We turned in early and next morning we rose as usual, but the dawn was misty and dark and thunder sounded hollowly in the mountains. Peta looked about and sniffed the air for a few minutes and then dismissed the omens: it was probably raining higher up, he remarked. Surely, I said, the creeks will flood. He thought they might, but only slightly, turning away to unhook some meat from the shelter.

Then at ten it began to drizzle but there was no wind. We did not let it worry us, and all set to work on the lines, each cutting a section to finish the job. In the evening we came back and the rain began to drop heavily, the big drops sounding on the rocks and drumming on the shelter. Both Misterisaac and I had returned, but Peta was still out somewhere cutting. As he came up the slope he stopped every so often, looked up at the sky, around at the creeks and at the hills. I wondered if he estimated that the rains were going to be serious, and I asked him as soon as he reached us. He looked out at the downpour, his body glowing ochre in the rainy light, wavering with rivulets and sparkling where the drops hit his shoulders. Behind him lay the ochre scene of sand and somewhere a frog croaked. He said he did not know about the rains.

"You say they come top side," I said.

"Me no know—now come this side."

"Fall heavy?"

"Me no know," he said, and the frogs began an intermittent chorus.

I felt uneasy at his attitude: it was so unlike an Indian, this not knowing. Maybe the rain would be for a week, maybe for only a few days, how could I know? I relied on them, particularly on Peta. Peta came out of the rain and sat on his hammock, letting the water drip fitfully from him, looking at his toes and licking the damp from his lips. This was the Peta I remembered, fighting calmly for his life above the falls, one of the braves; and on this trip he had shown nothing but mature responsibility. I had thought that perhaps he was glad to get away from the others just to show what a man he was for his young years—he was only seventeen or so—and now I was puzzled by this, which had come, like so many estrangements in life, not in angry words or scenes, but as the swift falling-away of unseen supports in a look and a word. Time was drawing on to the end of the year, to the big pay-day when, Peta knew, he would be getting a gun. Maybe he had worked hard for that: cutting the lines, digging pits, summoning his skill and defeating the jaguar. But now I wondered what his motives were.

The rain was heavy the next day and the water came slowly in the creeks, here and there drawing the sand, which fell in little avalanches from the banks. The landscape was crumbling before our eyes under the impersonal rain. Misterisaac was down in the creek washing and he came scampering up to say in halting words that plenty of water would lodge in this bowl if the rains came heavily and we should move camp up the spur behind. I sent Peta to look and give his judgment, but he returned and said he did not know. I surmised that he felt that, if he agreed on the danger, I would move out immediately: then he would have to carry a heavy load on a hard trail. There could be no other reason for his attitude. I now began to see that Peta had worked too well, had finished every task in time; when we had cut lines he had always gone on to do just the bit extra. I was relieved, in a way, for it was clear to me that he had hoped to ensure that at the full moon we could clear out with the task complete. When he saw the rain he had, it seemed, become afraid for the success of his intention. Misterisaac, I could see, understood all this and was aching to talk his head off, to agree with my forebodings; but I had depended on Peta and did not want to disgrace him by now turning to Misterisaac for guidance.

I called to Peta softly. He came smiling and I suggested we move camp. He agreed grudgingly, and I looked at him.

168

"Sometime, this place old savannah?"

"Sometime, maybe," he agreed.

It was no use, I could see, questioning him further, and we began moving camp that evening, making two or three trips with the stores. We found a good spot on the spur for a camp, but now food was our problem: we would have to hunt such birds as remained about in the rain, and I looked again at the sandhills through the haze. The water oiled along and trickles spread about from the creeks; I knew then certainly that it was a graveyard for water, a dried-up swamp of rounded boulders and water-moulded sand-banks surrounded by quickly rising hills and the solid green of jungle. One could climb out of that place and walk for forty days without meeting a soul. We could be cut off, as the worst parts lay between us, the village and the frontier. If we took to the mountains behind and circled round we might meet the big rivers in flood, as bad a situation as I had been in before.

I looked for my plug of Brazilian tobacco for solace. I had no cigarette paper, but the Indians beat the skin of a particular tree and strip off a transparent bark, as thin as cigarette paper but stronger, which is dried in the air, not over a fire. I kept squares of the bark handy in a tin, so I now pulled one out, ground the tobacco and stuck the paper down with saliva. As soon as the cigarette is stuck it must be smoked, so that the heat draws out the sap and forms a cement with the spittle. Brazilian plug tobacco is strong, black and moist; it keeps well in the jungle so long as it is in the plug and is a more satisfying smoke than machine-made cigarettes, which dry in the hills too easily. Often I found the Brazilian weed so sticky that it was better to take some and dry it slightly on a shovel over the fire, to make it milder. The Indians never refuse a cigarette or a butt and even stick a butt in a tree hole or some hiding place for future pleasure.

We all lay in our hammocks and started talking on a brighter note, discussing what we would eat on the morrow and deciding that we might find a powice early in the morning on the mountainside, although the rain might have driven them higher. All the time the rain thrummed and pattered and beat without respite, pinning in the sound of our voices and the smoke, which hung blue in a little patch about our home in the drowning greyness. We shot a few birds in the next few days, and as a precaution, I smoked all we could spare. Every morning the scene below had changed and fresh creeks appeared while old ones found new sinuous courses. The water was being held in the plain, because the rain was almost certainly falling below as well as above, so choking the channels that might otherwise have led it away. In such a place to watch the water rise inch by inch was more ominous than if it had roared by in thousands of gallons. I suggested on impulse that we drop everything and get out as we stood. Peta disagreed and suggested going by a roundabout way through the mountains. Then, I pointed out, if the rain stopped the others would come and find us gone. Misterisaac remained unmoved, his cheek bulging and moving with the usual cassava bread, his flanks spattered with the customary mud, scratching. Three days passed after the full moon and no Indians came. I suggested the others had found they could not reach us. Peta looked up, frankly, for the first time.

"Yes," he half whispered, "bottom side plenty water now."

I had nothing to say. I knew the Indians would not think of finding a long way round: they would measure the situation by their standards and assume that we could look after ourselves, for three months if need be. As I thought it over in the following days, the rains really began in earnest, in endless sheets, so that it was impossible to hunt and the plain became a vast lake. Soon hardly anything was to be seen except an odd tree rising out of the rain-pocked waters. We had food, although the camp was damp, and altogether I felt it was a better situation than I had faced on my own when I had last been in a flood. We had made a fire of great green logs end to end over a hot blaze until the fire entered the logs and burned inside them. In this method they are like the carbons of an arc lamp, only needing to be pushed together occasionally to maintain the heat, and they remain impervious to the hardest rain. Out of this kind of fire, which will last for two weeks or more, we drew the priming for a smaller, open blaze to cook over under the shelter. We kept also a stack of lily leaves which were slipped into the roof by any of us who should notice a leak. Sometimes I lay with nothing else to do but spend half an hour steering a drip from one leaf to another to the bottom of the roof; nothing seemed more annoying than a drip bouncing on the ground in the camp, even if it was doing no harm—it violated the ramparts we maintained against the flood.

In the mornings the boys walked up and down the banks of the water and looked for game, but there was none. We considered cutting woodskins to float out, but a woodskin only holds one person, which meant a mishap would be serious, especially as there could be no halt on the way owing to the lack of game. We did not consider a canoe: it would have been easy to make, although it would have taken a longer time than woodskins. We still based our ideas on the assumption that the rain would stop in a few days. We dared not march through the flooded land: we might walk all day and be still in water at night, unable to camp, and there was a great risk of snakes. No Indian will walk in a swamp through the night unless it is clearly a matter of life or death. I had to start rationing the food after a while, as Misterisaac continued to eat as if he were at home. We were now into the second week of the flood. By breaking up all the cassava bread I made a dole of one piece in the morning and one in the evening, and did the same thing with the meat.

CHAPTER ELEVEN

The Way Out

Days began to pass, with Peta dozing in his hammock and Misterisaac squatting beside me. Some days I could count the total of the few words spoken by either of them: they were retreating into themselves and storing energy. A silence descended on us and left us to our thoughts, as if the three of us, instead of being huddled together on a mountainside, were in our separate houses.

In the village, silence and separateness had been restoring to the spirits—the more so because of the confined company—but here, where each depended on the others for life, the new estrangement sapped and strained. The Indians were behaving naturally and I could not accuse them of wilful iciness; they become grave and cold in times of stress, and make brief innuendoes to each other to create a new mood of purpose. In this peculiar conversation between Peta and Misterisaac, remarks were followed by long intervals, and I felt isolated just when I needed moral support.

Peta lay in his hammock and Misterisaac squatted by the ashes staring blankly into space. They appeared to ignore me but they could not, for the fact was that they could not make their peculiar search for leadership without taking me into account. So whenever I turned my head or moved, Misterisaac's eyelids flickered in surreptitious glances. Peta lay swinging in his hammock and began to flip the sand with a wand. Hours passed, as I hoped somehow for a meeting of minds on the course we should take to get out, but Peta went on flicking the sand and muttering something to Misterisaac, who grunted without looking round.

"Look how the sand is bending this leaf," Peta murmured.

Misterisaac grunted again.

I recalled times at the village, such as the occasion once when a man had sat alone by a bush playing with a frog. He had worked the frog up to perform antics in the sand until he had magnetised the attention of the others, who soon forgot themselves and began to scream with laughter at the show. They slid into the hands of the conductor of the frog's dance, and in no time he had achieved a hold over them in a manner intensely satisfying to the Indian mind. When the height of the performance was reached, the man rose and walked away, leaving the others in an excited state. He went to his hut and took a bowl of cassili, his expression one of pride. I looked at him closely and he understood that I had not fallen under the spell and turned away: this had happened many times with others.

Peta was trying to pass a similar magnet before us to draw our minds into a harmony suitable to the occasion, but Misterisaac was not willing to yield. He got up and stood by his hammock with a self-conscious smile on his face.

"I am hungry," he said.

"The water is high enough. Why don't you get some fish?" said the thwarted Peta with some sarcasm.

Misterisaac cursed him, and they turned sour on each other.

Peta began to laugh softly, playing with the old man.

The silence drifted on and they relaxed. Finally Peta raised himself up and looked out of the shelter.

"I am hungry, too," he said simply.

Misterisaac laughed this time, imagining Peta offered an apology.

They went on like this, jostling for position in their mental tennis, confusing the issue frequently by speaking the truth: for we were all hungry.

"Let's sit down here and see what food we have," I suggested. "We should think of what day we can get out too."

Peta turned.

"Water high—we make canoe? We make canoe?" he said, again with a trace of sarcasm. I realised that he was touchy about any suggestion that threw responsibility on him: perhaps he had a guilty conscience over having delayed our departure too long.

His shifting moods and defiance made it impossible to lay hold of him. I could have tried a sensible conversation with Misterisaac, but I knew that Peta would counteract any influence I had with the old man, and the last thing I wanted was for them to leave me, for without them I would be finished. I had to find some common ground for conversation, and so fell back on the old dodge of a gift: I rolled three cigarettes and gave each of them one. They both smiled.

"Yapung, what time we go?" asked Peta at once.

I bent over the ash without replying and lit my cigarette.

"Two-three days," suggested Misterisaac.

"Maybe, maybe, sometime," I said, falling into their idiom. I had passed the onus of responsibility and did not want to speak any more. They were where I wanted them: about to think of ways to get out. I was beginning to react like them; I

174

even followed the Indian manner and did not offer my ember to light their cigarettes: having lit mine, I threw the ember back into the fire for them to pick up in turn.

I turned over the problem in my mind. They were accustomed to the hardship of our situation, but I knew that I could not get out alone. They could have stayed there a year, digging out the moles, eating the roots, ferreting out the worms and insects. I resigned myself, and prepared also to eat such things and to live their life completely, if it meant remaining alive, yet while playing the Indian rôle I had to come back to being myself every so often. If I had not, they would have come to look on me as being as independent as they were, and might take the attitude of "every man for himself" and set off on a course I could not follow.

After we had lit our cigarettes, Misterisaac went out and brought in his pouch of cassava bread, which he threw on the sand, instead of placing it politely before me.

"*Amora-wombe?* You hungry?" he asked pleasantly, but in the same tone he would use to another Indian, as if I were one.

"*Yawaik*—yes," I said.

He turned his back on me and began talking to Peta.

"We don't have much food," I heard him say.

"Maybe I go into the mountain to find a bird to shoot. Yapung is hungry," he continued. The rain had lessened and it was a feasible plan.

He was trying to avoid my suggestion of further rationing: an Indian cannot stomach rationing of any sort. As with all else, they must eat till satiated. However, Misterisaac came over when I pulled out all my food, and began to divide it, and he was all smiles at the prospect of a gift. I called for everything, and when they brought it I split it into three portions.

"Peta, *amora* food—your food. Misterisaac *amora*. You eat all now—good." I tapped my stomach. "One hour nothing. Two hour nothing."

They grabbed their shares out of the sand and began at once to eat without saying a word, as if they were starving; dur-

175

ing the evening they ate half their store. I ate a little and put the rest in the roof. When they were finished they became much brighter. They poked the fire into life and came together to my hammock, where I was lying.

"Yapung, one day time we make woodskin," suggested Peta. I knew that it was impossible to make a woodskin and get out of the floods safely as, if there was a spill, there was no bank to swim to. But now that they were filled they were making positive suggestions.

"Tonight we eat the *aki* and then hunt the labba," I said. I knew that when night came they would eat once more and that I would have to share out my remaining stores. They agreed, as the rain had ceased for a time, leaving a wet mist.

As I was cleaning my gun that evening, Peta went out of the camp and stood on a rise by himself. He began to hum a tune, broke off a small branch from a bush, looked at the sky and sang, while tapping the branch by his feet. When he had finished, he bent his head and hissed some words intensely. Misterisaac had turned his back and I did the same, realising that he was making an invocation against the evil spirits which had brought misfortune upon us, so that we should make a good hunt or make our way safely out of the region.

This action recalled the *pi-eye* dance at the death of Labba's father, and many other events. It illustrated the philosophy of the Indians, who believed that life is wholly good in its natural state and can only be spoiled by evil influences, evil being a dissipation of the life force and the ritual of beating a summoning of purpose within themselves against it. This motif runs through all their ceremonies. Beating branches round a sick man, the rhythm of the tapped foot, the beating of the ceremonial fish on the guests before a feast, the flexing of muscles and intense words between clenched teeth, are goads to liven the will and to live once more with positive and unified intent. This being so, the act of invocation is not directed straight at the "evil spirits," but is a masochistic call upon their own resources. The conception of evil is a convenient personification and the projection of the lack of holiness within themselves. In fact they define their ideal of positive living negatively, by emphasizing the existence only of spirits which are evil. When evil is removed, what is left is the good.

Such invocations, being directed at their inner selves, are secretive acts: the others around should not hear too much and they must turn away. There is some similarity between this wishing, particularly by the sick bed, and the silent prayer one makes at the sight of someone in danger—when a tightrope walker sets out to rolling drums under the circus tent, and everyone hopes, almost physically, that he will reach the other side. It seems part of human nature that such a wish, to be effective, should be almost, but not quite, private. The prayer may be directed at a god, but in fact the concentration is rarely on the deity but on the actor himself, and on the wish that he will summon all his faculties for success. The wisher identifies himself with the sufferer and hopes, by living through his ordeal in tiny motions of the muscles, to help him. The Indian makes such acts of will not only for the welfare of others but on his own behalf, as Peta was doing. After his invocation Peta came into the shelter, now happy and resolved.

"Yapung, we go mountain. We shoot labba. We get! We get!"

"You want cigarette?" I offered one to each of them. It kept up their spirits and, in any case, it was a hunting rule to finish smoking before moving out to the hunting ground, to prevent the scent being carried. We sat puffing while I sorted out the ammunition, and then we set off for the mountain slope on the most dangerous form of hunting—by night without flares.

We sought some lana trees, which produced a fruit prized by the labba. I had thought the safest plan would be to sit in a tree and wait for one to come, but when I had climbed my tree the others did not follow. They wormed their way about in the undergrowth for some time and then Misterisaac sat on a rock, an unusually low position for night hunting. It was not safe, but they had meant what they said and were determined to come back with a kill that night.

They stopped in one position only long enough to listen and sniff for snakes and for game, then they moved as softly as a cat to another position within an area twenty yards around the lana tree. If they were capable of locating and killing by ear alone in the dark, they would do it now. I thought how easily they might die in a whip of a bushmaster, a real and great risk from which there was no hope of recovery, and felt undeniable fear as well as exasperation at my lack of skill to assist them. Peta came below the lana tree and I could see him faintly, bending to feel where the lana fruit lay. He backed away, rubbing out his footprints and bending to sniff the ground, to see how recently a labba had been feeding there.

He climbed the lower branch of my tree and told me to wait where I was, while he crept away to the other side of the lana tree. They had moved about so much that human scent was everywhere, and his plan was to shoot as soon as the labba came within range—in the dark and out of sight. Both Peta and Misterisaac had felt about on all fours and mapped the whole area in their minds, and remembered the position of every bush, boulder, stick and pile of lana fruit. After many minutes the labba came—I could hear it brushing faintly through the undergrowth—and instinctively I faced towards the sound. Before I was positioned, Peta fired with my gun at the labba while it was still walking forward, taking an aim by ear, without seeing the animal, firing back towards us and a few degrees to one side. If he had missed, Misterisaac would have fired.

I heard Misterisaac drop his gun and scramble down into the darkness with an arrow in his hand.

"Emoaro! Emoaro!—He's there, there!" cried Peta.

"Yawetnung—I can't find it," Misterisaac shouted back.

Peta kept calling. Misterisaac floundered about and found the labba, still moving, and stabbed it repeatedly with the arrow until the arrow was broken. Now I felt that, in this spirit of determination, we would have a real chance of escaping from the sand-bowl, but first we must eat our fill. Usually an Indian ties up a kill carefully to carry it home, but now they slit the labba's throat savagely and dragged it back, Misterisaac being covered in blood. When we had hauled the kill into the camp I suggested cleaning it. They looked at me as if I had said something ill-mannered.

"Yapung, we eat everything. We throw nothing away," Peta said.

They were not going to prepare it in the usual way and quarter the carcass for the barbecue: all thirty pounds of the labba would be ours. The only loss would be about five pounds from smoking over the fire, for even the bones and hooves would make food. We carried the labba down to the water line, drained away the blood and washed it. Misterisaac slit open the stomach. Peta squatted downstream in all seriousness, cupping his hands to catch any entrails which floated away. The gut was cleaned of its contents and Peta took it in his lap to wash it.

They made a sausage of the big gut, packed with the heart, liver, lights and the rest, divided the carcass down the centre and cut off the head. The halves were put over the fire and the head and sausage by the fireside to smoke slowly. They had not scraped off the hair, lest any flesh was taken off with it, and the meat smelled rank, so I soused most of it with salt and we sat waiting for the first bit of meat that would be cooked. Without salt, I imagine the dish would be too revolting for most men. The Indian uses pepper to drown unwelcome tastes and carries a small bamboo vial of it, with a small hole in the top through which the peppers are dropped one by one and then pounded with a stick to a thick paste. It is his form of pepper mill. He plunges the stick in the vial and wipes it on each mouthful of meat. When the vial is exhausted it is given to the children, who break it open and ferret out the pepper from the corners to season their food.

We had been lucky to find the labba, as the rain started again, and after four days of sitting immobilised under the shelter all that was left was the head and hooves and the gut sausage. We had eaten all the rest, including the ribs and the leg bones, which, after they had been well scorched, can be crunched up in the teeth. Misterisaac suggested that I start on the head.

"The eyes are good," he said.

I was relieved when I pulled away the shrivelled lids and found that the heat had reduced the eyes to nothing. They ate the hooves, which were mostly of hard burned leather. I cleaned out the head and was so committed to the game by this time that, when it was finished, I proudly hung up the skull under the roof; it was picked clean and white. In fact, the tongue had tasted excellent and I had been able with a small stick to pick out many choice bits of meat. The next day I said we should not eat and keep the gut for the day after. They were in good spirits after eating well. Peta pointed to the mountains.

"Me get good eat," he said.

"*Waluk-mak?*—The edible white frog?" I asked.

"No, no."

They left in the rain and I remained behind. If it had not been raining we could have gone out for more labba, for during the day they hide in their holes and it is usual to smoke them out, but the rain prevented it. The Indians came back with the roots of the manico tree, a kind of palm of which the young roots are soft and sweet. They had found no frogs, but had a large leaf full of amora, which is the chrysalis of the cicada, a long white grub, which they had hooked out from behind the bark of trees. Their faces glistened with pleasure in anticipation.

"Come, Yapung, you eat now," they said.

"No, I can't eat this," I said.

They laughed heartily, for the first time in at least three weeks. Misterisaac was in great excitement and pointed to the grubs and the sausage with a shaking hand.

"You eat that one—then you eat this one. All same. That one big this one little. Same thing, same thing."

They began at once to thread the amoras on thin spikes and turn them over the fire until roasted. I contented myself with the roots, and they filled themselves with the amora. They began to get into a state of mind not uncommon among Indians when they relish all the oddest things that can be eaten. They left the gut, although it is a delicacy, and almost feverishly began to think of what else they could find. Peta got up and looked about the camp for flying ants, which gather in the jungle during wet weather and flutter in swarms under trees. Usually flying ants are a child's delicacy: whenever they swarm, the children run about popping them in their mouths with screams of delight. If an adult wants some of them he will not go out himself, but will send a child and eat the ants in private to avoid the ridicule of others. Although Peta and Misterisaac walked some way around the camp, they found none and returned tired. We found that we were beginning to feel the cold more than before and had to keep the fire blazing high for comfort. The rains kept pouring down the next day and we lay in our hammocks eating the remains of the sausage—our last meal for some time unless we had luck, so that it was now the hour when our decision must be made. We talked it over, and made up our minds that we would break out in the next two days, even if the water had not gone down. On Monday we ate nothing but roots and then the rain stopped. But, unknown to us, while it had been raining the water had gone down two feet because the rains had ceased lower down and the streams were carrying away the floods.

Peta suggested another night hunt, but I pointed out that after a day of sunshine all the snakes would be out hunting themselves and it would be doubly dangerous. That night we could hear the water tumbling over the many falls and then discovered the drop in the water level. The noise of crashing water grew as the drop of the falls increased; we were elated and forgot about hunting and ran down to the rocks to see which falls were exhausted first. The next day was the second without food, but I could see no sign of weakness in them: they seemed like camels which had stored nourishment, but I felt slightly faint and sick, having only my tobacco to kill the hunger pains.

On the third day the water was far enough down for us to skip from rock to rock. It was unsafe, as if the floods had returned suddenly we might have found ourselves far from the bank and cut off. But the new freedom was so inviting that we decided to make a break across the remainder of the swamps and try to reach a tree in which to sleep. We were now more than four weeks overdue, and I imagined that the villagers might have given up hope of our return. What I could not understand was why they had not made an expedition by building canoes at the side of the flood lower down and coming in for us. I was sure that it would have been possible, although hazardous. When we finally set off we did not have heavy loads, as all the food was finished and most of my clothes had long since become tattered and rotten beyond use. We carried only the sieves and shovels and I wore only a pair of shorts and walked barefoot.

We could not follow the trail cut by the two boys, as they had not considered floods and had struck down into gullies now deep in water. So we walked that day, the third without food, across the shallower parts of the swamps, across tree trunks and over the higher sandbanks. The others were ahead looking for shallow ground to keep moving. I suggested a rest as I could go no more. They also were weakening from the heavy going, which had frequently meant swimming for long stretches, pulling the *warishi* loads behind us. Ahead of us lay high ground and the higher plateau, but we were still in the area of the sandbowl and three or four miles to one side of the correct trail line which the boys had cut.

As we sat down I noticed how white and perished our skins had become from the long soaking in the camp and the immersion in water. Our feet particularly had the crinkled appearance of crepe rubber. We had picked up large water leeches and had neither the means nor the energy to remove them: there was a little salt left which, sprinkled on them, would have made them drop off, but I wanted to keep it. We had also collected ticks from the bushes and these we now picked off each other. But the leeches remained hanging from us like black chipolata sausages for the next three days.

Ahead was the bedraggled and mouldering jungle fringe —sappy pools, some black with rotting vegetation. Silence hung everywhere. Only the sun, gleaming here and there through the trees, shot through the pools to show how deep they were, and was an encouragement. Some pools were no more than eighteen inches deep but, where they lay in shade, their jet blackness made them appear bottomless; others stretched for several hundred yards and were deep, according to our estimation. By a knowledge of various trees and of the height at which the first branches normally sprouted, I and the others were able to judge fairly accurately the depth of these deeper pools.

When we had rested for a while, Peta went off ahead to scout the trail. He swam out of sight and soon the sounds of his movements ceased. He had been gone a long time when we heard a strangled cry from far away: the lack of food may have caused a hoarseness or it may have been excitement, but it was Peta calling us.

"Peta in trouble," I said.

We dropped our *warishis* and my gun fell in the water, but I left it as we scampered, splashed and swam after the sound. Misterisaac's quick ear picked up each shout at once and set him on course. Eventually we drew closer until the direction was clear. Misterisaac began to call and ask what was happening. Peta's voice came back and Misterisaac repeated his words with surprise. I caught the word *aki*—bake or a cake—before Misterisaac dashed off ahead and left me. In a few moments Peta appeared, swimming between the trees and pushing a huge gourd which floated low in the water. He was giving the wild Indian cry of joy or victory which I had heard at the beginning of the feast; it is rare to hear an Indian shouting like this, and when he does he is one of the happiest and most excited beings alive. When he reached me I smelt cassili. Peta had found the gourd in a tree with some meat and bakes which Misterisaac was bringing.

The gourd and food had been put there by the villagers. This was one of the most remarkable displays of Indian skill I witnessed: they had indeed come out to help us, but had worked out to the last detail the nature of our trouble before moving. They anticipated how the floods would behave and our movements in relation to them, before we ourselves had decided to escape by any particular route. They had picked on the route we would take in view of the lie of the land and there slung caches of food from the trees. But it was impossible to grasp how they could place the food exactly where it would be seen, yet it was not a matter of luck, for it happened twice and not on the line of any marked trail. It reminded me of the food put out for guests to the feasts: the trails to any village are many, but by some intuition the Indians are able to pick those which, according to the weather, the state of the jungle and other unaccountable factors, the incomers will follow. In our case their appreciation had demanded an acute eye for the lie of the land to pick the edge of the jungle where we would break out of the swamp.

Misterisaac appeared soon after, smiling from ear to ear, showing the comical gap in the front of his teeth, and splashing carelessly so that mud spurted the height of his waist. He carried meat and bakes which were sufficient for three or even four days' rations. We took the food back to where we had left the *warishis* and took long swigs of the cassili. It was sour and powerful, half mushy, as it becomes when turning from liquid into a fermented state. We tore at the meat and swallowed long strips quickly. After a hearty meal we packed the remains of the rations and trekked on, at a fast rate, and reached high ground that night, several hundred feet above the valley and on dry ground. We sat in front of a great fire and drank again from the huge gourd—it must have held three gallons—and finished the lot. We felt mightily relieved at paying no attention to each other's idiosyncrasies and lay about without a care, without even the sense to sling our hammocks above the reach of the kamodie snakes which slide about in such country at night. Our only movements were to help the man drinking to tip up the gourd, which we took in turn, and to let go with a loud satisfied belch. The effect was to warm one's inside and create an expansive, reckless mood, without actually fuddling the senses.

It was our only food for three days and we felt the first sense of contentment we had known for some time. I pulled out all my tobacco and flung it on the ground for them and they fumbled with it, trying to make cigarettes. Eventually I rolled them and we sat puffing the rich blue smoke, a happy little band, laughing and at ease in the jungle. We had escaped from the slough, had eaten and drunk and had no cares. A great feeling filled me that this was the only good way to live and I wished I could go on like this for the rest of my life.

Next day we walked onwards, taking the ridges and high ground to keep clear of the floods. The meat and bakes were soon finished but the huge gourd supplied us for another three days: when it was empty Peta said we should punch a hole in it and sink it in a pool, so that when the villagers came out hunting they would find it and be able to trace our trail. In good spirits we tramped on, without heeding the mud, pools and roots in our way. Although we had seen no snakes, Peta told me there were many about, particularly of the red-headed kind.

On the fifth day we reached a fine dry line for our trail, leading into the mountain we had to climb before reaching the plateau where the village lay. We knew that once on the mountain top we should be able to see signal fires, if the nights were clear, so we climbed all that night to the top. The moon was up but it was hard going on the steep slopes of loose stone and we pulled ourselves up on the vines. The moonlight, reflecting from the rocks on the wet vines gave them a living luminosity. Frequently I snatched a vine, only to loose it at once, fearing it was a red-head snake.

When we reached the top Peta said he would look ahead for a good camp site where we would sling our hammocks and sleep the whole day. When he had been gone about five minutes, he began shouting for us to come quickly. We picked up our traps and ran until I saw Peta squatting on the ground leaning back with a huge gourd to his mouth and the contents trickling over his chest. Around him lay more bakes and meat. I tapped him on the shoulder and he smiled but went on drinking, then came out for a second. "Me find! Me find!" he said and went under the gourd again.

We dragged him off and took our turns, repeating our lotus-eating party of a few days before. The trip out was assuming a timeless paradisaic air, by contrast to our previous hardships, and I became more decided to forget diamonds and live the life of the Indians. So we sat all night drinking until Mister-isaac began to complain of dysentery. I stopped him from drinking more at once, as the cassili was the obvious cause. It is one of the few serious Indian complaints which they only aggravate by drinking more. I told him that in the morning he must go up the hill and find the quazouk chinak, a vine which is good for dysentery, to eat. Next day was our last alone and we reached the village by nightfall, welcomed by them all and glad to be home again.

CHAPTER TWELVE

Hunters' Time

ABOUT two months after our escape the dry season was well advanced, but the village had been so disturbed by my previous prospecting, including the trip to the sandhills, that food was short. Spirits were low, the land was baked and cracked and the game had gone out of the hills to the pools and grottoes higher up, where the animals had made new hides and the mountain cats were eating their fill. This was the season when the Indians live wholly as hunters, dispersing from the village and leaving it bare, moving out into the hills with all the cunning and skill they know. There, each small group of men and their families becomes a party on its own, hunting and killing and eating as they move around the headwaters of the rivers and creeks after the small game. On their return they hope to bring back to the village the big game, the deer and the labba, cut in quarters to smoke and store in the houses. Before this time the Indians are often at their lowest ebb, allowing the village to become dirty, sitting about, cracking old gourds to scrape out cassili, the children munching the last scraps of cassava bread, now blue with mould.

The barbecues were searched for old bones and scraps and there were no fish in the traps; no longer did the smell of fresh baking waft over the village from the *aki* house, and all was stale and musty. Around the camp fire at night we ate the foulest dregs from the cassili canoe and talked of big things, murmuring not of going out for a day's hunting, but of working far into the hills. The new boys, Cassequak—which means Turtle, or Slow and Cunning One—and Cuchang—Long One —spoke of going to the Copenang, a region near the Brazilian frontier known for its good hunting, to which other tribes would go, but their wives were against it, as they were afraid that the boys wanted to go back to their own people—a step which they might consider taking even though the need for hunting had become urgent. Peta and Labba suggested going down to the low ground where it is always damp.

As the men spoke up, the women stood behind, darting their eyes towards any who had a suggestion to make; the children were not in their hammocks but leaned on posts, listening with pouting mouths and round eyes to know when they might eat again. For three or four nights the tense and serious talk continued, while in the daytime preparations for the hunting went ahead. The women collected the last of the food, including the few remaining vegetables from the farms, so that everyone could leave with a full stomach, for once on the journey there would be perhaps a week without solid food. Fortunately I had a small stock of condensed milk which I ate with some greens and corn.

The men went out to cut new bows, sometimes searching

for an hour to find a root of the type of mango tree they use which was wiry and strong enough, and testing its springiness by holding it on the ground and wrapping a leg round it to twist with powerful calves. The bows are taller than the Indians, some as much as six feet six inches, and the arrows longer still, the heaviest being seven feet six inches, and for many weeks in the hills I was unable to bend the bows more than an inch or two, but the Indians can hold them on a steady aim at full stretch for a minute or more. The power of these weapons is considerable, and with the long arrow heads, some seven inches with four barbs, they can strike mortally, and with accuracy and silence, at anything that moves. The arrow heads are of hard yari-yari wood blackened in the fire, or sometimes of iron: the yari-yari being as effective as steel but only able to be used once. They spend days filing a bit off the barrel of an old *pibung* with another piece of iron, then beat it and beat it until it takes on a shape one would imagine could only be achieved with a forge and anvil. All about the village the men were busy at these tasks, hammering, bending and testing, shaving the bows and the arrows with their hunting knives, running their hands, greasy with meat, along the shafts, smoothing them here and there until they were in perfect shape and glistening bright.

When the weapons were ready, the women began to renew the scars on the men, made as charms for hunting. Each man was known for his skill at hunting some particular game, and his cuts were made accordingly, usually six lines from elbow to wrist and five from elbow to shoulder, into which they rubbed a potion called a *beana*. The *beana* varied, but were usually a mixture of herbs with some bone or tissue of the animal ground into them: there was the *mypuri beana*, the *labba beana*, the deer *beana*, and a snake *beana* of a protective nature. The village bustled with women carrying small bamboo gourds of *beana* about and the men stood around while the blood congealed. I waited to see whether I would be included.

After the two young boys had had their *beana* cuts in front of me, Peta came over. "Yapung, good *beana, kapung beana*—Indian charm." He stood with a handful of vials and held them out for me to smell. "You hunt, you see good, you smell good, you hear good. You always see game before it sees you." This I found hard to believe, although it is true that Indians out hunting become more astute and sensitive than the wiliest game afoot. When I agreed to have the *beana*, Peta produced some crushed bone and small curved teeth, which reminded me of those of a young alligator: it was the head of a bushmaster snake baked and kept for a long time. Mixed with the bone was gunpowder, a strong-smelling herb, like ginger, and a dark liquor with tiny Guinea pepper seeds. He poured some of this watery paste into a small bowl and added some water, saying that I was to drink the liquid in one gulp. I hesitated, but was reassured, all the villagers standing round with serious expressions, so I swirled the mixture round and swallowed. A wave of sulphurous fumes burst in my head and I shuddered from the indescribable peppery taste.

He next made me stand on tiptoe and when my ankle muscles were tense made a circular cut with his knife below my ankle bone and gripped my instep while he rubbed in the paste. It burned for a moment or two, and then Peta told me that I was safe from the bushmaster snake. The process was a form of crude vaccination, but I had yet to find out its effectiveness. Later that day Peta gave me scratches on my calf for hunting the deer and I was as well prepared as the rest.

Then there was a *beana* I had known about for some time. On a previous hunt, when we were seeking pigs on a misty morning, we smelt many hogs nearby—an Indian can smell them a mile away, but even I could pick them out on this hunt. There was no need to say a word: everyone flexed his bow or cocked his gun and went after them across the savannah. We came upon a big herd and all fired almost at the same moment, killing over a dozen. Hogs are known to be dangerous a long while after they appear to be dead, so they were tied up securely, with a knot around the mouth and the feet fastened together and strapped to the body, and carried into camp for the women to cut up. One of the hogs was a female, and in slitting open its stomach Labba's mother came across a tight, browny-grey ball of hairs and tiny pieces of vegetable matter about the size of a tennis ball. She did not touch it, for this was one of the most powerful aids to hunting and only a man might handle it. Peta came over and took it out to show me.

"This good *beana*," he said. "One day I show you how to use it." It was this hog *beana* called *pingo* that Peta now produced for our present hunt. The ball had shrunk to the size of a golf ball and was firm enough to be cut neatly in half: he handed me one piece to carry and gave the other to another party. These *pingo beanas*, which are accumulations of indigestible matter, are rarely found and are greatly prized for use on the hunt itself. He told me that when hunters meet a large herd of pigs and the hogs scatter, there may be a confusion of tracks to follow and a widespread scent. In this case a bit of the *pingo beana* is put on some dry earth and lit. Thin smoke will rise and suddenly bend in one definite direction, attracted, said Peta, by the nearest hogs: if that pointer is followed, a kill is almost certain. How this indeed appeared to be true I was to see several times later.

Finally the fires were doused, the doors of the houses shut with chinak thongs and the tame animals and birds left to fend for themselves on scraps. Labba, Peta, Cassequak and Cuchang with their wives formed one party, which I joined, the young wives having woven new *warishis* for us all, to carry the meat. We were the strongest party, the men fully armed with heavy bundles of arrows at their backs, new *saloes* and spare ones tucked at their waists as a concession to their wives, their weapons shining with newness, and with an air of purpose in their light Indian steps. We set off to the east and the rest of the village dispersed, each party taking a different direction without plan, choosing a route they saw was still vacant; those with small children intending to go the shortest distance.

It was hot, dry and crisp and the jungle rustled and crackled, but we preferred these noisy conditions and sped along the tracks careless of being heard. The women kept up easily, wearing their full dress of beads which, besides being decorative, was the most practical costume. We aimed to cross two ranges of mountains and had no intention of trying to hunt on the way, merely going as far, by Indian calculations, as the game from the grounds around the village would have travelled, so we made hurried camps each night, living solely off farine. Soon we reached damper jungle where the trees were so thick that the sun came through only in a dull green gleam.

We had travelled three days without sight or sound of game, noticing that the young shoots on which the animals feed were dry and stunted—a sign of a bad season. The only life were many white-faced monkeys, one or two baboons and marmosets. After travelling through many gloomy valleys, keeping on low ground where trails would be clear, beyond the second range from the village, we reached a small ravine down which a trickle of water ran, cutting a way through a thick carpet of mouldering leaves. The going was slippery and the hidden roots threatened a sprained ankle. Suddenly we came across heavy tracks about eighteen inches deep in the leaves, crossing the ravine and going towards the flats, below where ferns grew among sandhills.

Peta and Labba decided to investigate the tracks that night while the rest of us camped on the flats. We made a little fire and settled down to sleep, but I could hear the other two moving up and down in the ravine with iowa gum flares. They came in just before dawn and told us they had worked out that they were the tracks of a large mypuri female with a young one: they had traced the hoof scratches on roots, noted which branches had been broken and had followed the tracks over the hill until they reached ground about a mile distant, where clear prints showed in earth. Their plan was to leave this game for the present and come back to it when we had made kills of small game further on, as they knew that if we did not disturb the mypuri we should be able to return and pick it up several days later, as the mother would not go far with its young.

During the next day we began to find plenty of birds and shot many powice and maams which were feeding on the nuts and seeds growing on the damp ground; having no utensils for boiling, we roasted them and had a good fill, which heartened everyone. On the next day we reached a fine region with many tracks and also trail-blazing by other Indians. This was no surprise and the marks were identified as being those of the Macoushi, who must have been hunting with bows also, as otherwise we should have heard their guns by this time. We made a small benabu palm-leaf camp and roasted more birds, keeping the eggs for me, as the Indians never eat them, since eggs either remind them of fat, which they detest, or they think that eating them means fewer birds and is therefore wasteful. The women were to stay in camp while we sallied out individually to cover a wide area. We chose various markers up the mountain spur in front of us—a tall tree, a shoulder of the hill—to mark off each man's ground, and spread out.

When an Indian starts hunting, his manner and walk changes. He lifts his feet higher and steps more lightly, each muscle under complete control, so that he seems to flow through the jungle like a tiger. The long arrows at his back, too long to be carried in a quiver, do not impede him and never catch on branches. When he smells or hears something, he freezes and stops in whatever position he may be in—with one hand raised, holding a branch where it brushed him, or with a foot half off the ground. His neck extends, his mouth is open, he looks about without moving his head, listening. When he is tired he chooses a place from where there is a view in three directions for at least twenty-five yards and sits with his back against a tree or guarded by a thicket—the safest position in the jungle. To the hunting Indian, time is of no account and all that matters are the many signs he notices of game. He may sight several traces of animals nearby but reject them as unsuitable: a deer's track, for instance, going towards the mountains, would not normally be followed, as the deer is in its element among the high slopes and is hard to corner for a shot.

The essence of Indian hunting is calculation, not merely the ability to draw and aim, although that is hard enough in the jungle. For as soon as the hunter is in game country, his acute senses will tell him every minute of different animals, of their size, how long they waited in different spots, and their course, so that soon the Indian must weigh up which to pursue; after that the chase becomes a battle of wits between himself and the game until he tricks it into a position from where he can shoot at close range. Only one emotional consideration comes into the hunt; when the hunter realises there are two animals nearby from which to choose, he will not pursue the largest or the easiest to kill, but the one whose meat he most favours. The wild hog is the favourite of most, as it contains little fat.

While the other men went off in their different directions, I started on my hunt and soon found the tracks of a deer, which continued up to a spur and became too faint for me to follow. It was midday by this time, when I ought to return unless I had a sure kill in sight. In coming back I saw an acouri—a small, quick-witted golden animal about the size of a rabbit; it is the most sensitive animal in the jungle, which sees a hunter as quickly as he notices it. Acouris will sit munching a nut, watching the man, darting for a few steps should he move, and eating again. I knew that if I raised my arm with my gun he would run out of sight at once, and if I did not act carefully he could have me dodging about among the trees taking fresh aims on him until he had finished his nut, when he would go for good. I was holding my gun in my right hand, parallel with the ground, so I slowly put my finger on the trigger, moved the gun upwards slightly and fired at the same time. The shot spread and caught him. A habit of the acouri is to yell at the top of his voice even if only one pellet touches him, and this one did so now, although in this case with justification, as he was, in fact, mortally hit. He ran only a few steps and collapsed, dead. This and another acouri were my only kills, a poor showing by Indian standards, although acouri meat is the best for drying and keeping and was useful to us on that account.

Cassequak and Cuchang came back, but Peta and Labba did not return for two days, so we realised that they must be close on the trail of some big game and looked forward to hearing how they had fared, without hammocks and therefore unable to sleep except in snatches at the foot of a tree. The In-

194

dians know that no animal will go more than a day away from its grazing ground, and are prepared to keep up with it for that length of time at least, or even to get far enough in front of it, having judged its future course, to be able to direct it to the place they have chosen for the kill. This is the true nature of hunting—a form of driving which never becomes so out of hand as to frighten the animal into real flight. We supposed that the two men were performing this particular feat.

When they returned they told us of their trip, and it was as we had imagined. They had come on the trail of a deer, and were working it together, Peta on one side and Labba on the other—a position in which they had moved after following the tracks and turning off from them at right angles, then circling round to come abreast with the deer, sliding and hurrying silently through the jungle. There was much difficult country about, and they purposely allowed the deer to get wind of them so that it could be driven: the deer knew that it was being hunted and kept stopping, like the men, to check on the other's position. They began to force it away from the routes of escape towards a narrow stony gully where its movements would be slower, for a deer likes to run on soft ground where its hooves are not jarred. Although Peta and Labba were out of sight and hearing of each other, they communicated through the movements of the deer: when the deer turned to the left Labba knew that Peta was coming in close to him on the other side and so he gave ground to keep away from him; where the ground favoured a turn to the right, Labba would close in and Peta would hear the deer and move away in turn. So they drove the big beast on and kept in position on the wings of the chase.

On their way they saw other tracks, some of a number of labba feeding nearby. They glanced at trees and estimated as they went how they might return and make *wabinis* for a night shoot. In this way they took notice of all useful signs for future hunting, without losing the deer, ignoring powice and other birds, lest the sound even of a bow shot and the scurry of a bird were to frighten the deer. At the end of the day it stopped and the crisis was at hand: this was the moment when it knew that its reserves were becoming exhausted and when it might turn and break out in a run.

Labba and Peta now started whistling to each other and the deer heard this strange noise from behind it, first from one side and then from the other, and decided not to make a dash for it. It could not climb the mountain before it. It turned to one side and heard the whistle, and then to the other, only to hear it again. Labba and Peta moved about tormenting it with short hollow calls so that it became confused in its tiredness. Labba alone now made the calls and Peta took the arrows from his back, which were fastened in the usual spiral of chinak which he released by pulling a thong. He chose a long, heavy arrow and prepared to shoot if the deer broke out on his side; but the deer did not move and they knew it was getting into the bemused state they desired. They were silent and the deer stood sniffing the air about it, no more than a hundred yards from the hunters, who had closed in and could see the movement of the bushes where it stood. They would not shoot at this moment when it was still undecided and nervous, but waited for an hour, sitting at the foot of trees to see whose will would prevail, theirs or the deer's. In their place I would have fired long before, but only at the risk of wounding and losing it: they were prepared to work for a certain shot and sat on with their bows held as lightly as feathers in the crooks of their arms.

Finally the deer relaxed and began to walk away slowly. This was the unguarded moment for which they had waited: to shoot now would certainly throw the deer into confusion and it would become an easy target for a second shot. The deer believed that it was no longer followed, but its mind had become conditioned to the direction it would now take and it went slowly towards the ravine the men had chosen for it, so they continued to hold their fire. They got up quietly and left the deer, circling round, went in easy strides to the ravine and sat down close to each other. The deer was free but it walked towards them, while they took their arrows and fitted them without hurry to their bows. When it came in sight, its antlers raised, their bows were at full stretch and they fired together,

196

striking it straight in the chest as it walked up to them, still sure that any danger was behind and that the narrow gully was safe.

That fine deer gave us plenty of meat: it was unusually large and one leg filled a *warishi*. There were the mypuri still to be killed, and so we set out on the way back, now in the second week of the hunt, during which I had eaten almost nothing but meat. About a mile from the mypuri tracks we smelt hogs, and then we heard people talking and laughing ahead. I sent Labba to see who they were. He came back and said they were two Macoushi who had seen our tracks and knew from them that there was a stranger with the Patamona. We reached an old man and a youth sitting on a log looking at the ground pretending to be disinterested—the usual way for Indians to behave when they are curious. The old man had two strings of hog's teeth and I knew he must be a renowned hunter of the hog; both of them were well armed with many collapsible arrows at their waists. We spoke to them in Patamona, asking them how they were, and they understood and made non-committal replies. Then they asked where we had shot the deer. In answer to our questions they said that they had come from a long hunt and were weary: this did not ring true, and I was even more suspicious when the old man said that night was coming quickly and that we should find our camps soon.

As we walked away the scent of the hogs became stronger and we realised they were trying to put us off hunting them, as they were waiting to make a slaughter of the big pack with their collapsible arrows, but as there were bound to be enough for all of us it seemed no crime to make our own hunt. One of the girls became excited and whispered to Peta, "*Pingo, pingo.*" Peta went on without replying. Everyone knew the situation by his own nose and there was no need to discuss it. We went on for half a mile, knowing the Macoushi must be peeping at us from behind to see where we went, and when we had crossed the hill ahead, halted and unhitched the *warishis*. I made eight cartridges with my brass cases and put in them the heaviest slugs I had. Peta took Misterisaac's *aragebuza* which had been carried by one of the women and I gave him some powder, using bits of my shirt for wadding.

We decided that the women would stay with the *warishis* and went on until we could hear the hogs snapping their teeth a short distance away. Just then we heard the squeal of several hogs and knew the Macoushi had lost no time and had begun to fire from another direction. The herd began to scatter, since the Macoushi were shooting in such a way as to break it up so that it had no leader, and the groups would move slowly and aimlessly, an easy prey for further shots. The bulk of the herd was moving off before the Macoushi towards the mountains we had just left and we decided to hunt the ones left in front of us, which were fanning out in groups of four or five, trying to find the main herd. Peta decided to use the *pingo beana* to pick out one lot, so I took the *beana* from my bag and broke off a bit and placed it on a small cone of earth at the root of a tree. When I lit it, it began to burn like incense with a thin, dense column of smoke. We stood back being careful not to breathe on it, and when the smoke had risen about eighteen inches it leaned away to one side, as they had said it would, and fanned out into the air. As soon as it took this bend we stamped it out and followed that course. Almost at once, without varying from the line, we came across three hogs and shot them with the guns and by the bows. We went on and shot three more and decided to call a halt, as we had more than enough to carry and, after a day's rest, we went in easy stages back to the village. That was our hunt.

CHAPTER THIRTEEN
Adopted

I was sitting by my window one day, gazing down the slope to the creek. The sun beat down, a breeze combed the water and rippled in light green waves across the belt of young cassava below the village, and all was quiet and asleep. Cuchang came out of his hut and walked away from the village, stopping every few paces to look ahead with a fixed gaze as if to attract attention. He circled the village, crossing the trails leading to the creek and the farms, going over rough ground. Mikme, a plump bow-legged little girl, and two boys came out of their houses and waddled after him, their hair hanging down like

199

mops, looking for a game or the pleasure of watching a grown-up.

He stopped and looked back at the children. *"Me-aley, me-aley*—go back." Mikme fingered her beads and bent her head, smiling and looking at him. Cuchang dodged into his house and came out at once carrying two fishing-rods; Mikme walked slowly back with the boys shooting glances over her shoulder. The fishing rods added to the oddness, as it was not the fishing season and there was nothing to catch in the creek. Mikme bobbed into her house and piped, *"Marouk, marouk*—to fish." No one stirred. Cuchang came past my house and sat on a stump, the rods between his open legs and splayed his feet. He sat for about fifteen minutes by turns looking at the ground and glancing up, his thin face slightly uncertain, without drawing on the sand with his rods as Indians usually do.

The outer door of one of the houses swished open. Amelia stepped out, her large firm breasts gleaming in the sun, and flung her head up, her hair falling down her stocky back. She walked slowly towards the creek, Mikme and the boys following her, as children usually follow a woman going to the creek, where she might show them how to swim. Cuchang did not move his head but glanced sideways at Amelia, who was his wife. "Mikme, *oitka, oitka*—come," she said softly to the children, without looking at them, although they were already behind her.

As she went into the waving cassava she appeared to be naked in a green sea, only her breasts and hair showing above. Below, the creek slid by heavily and her broad back glistened in a shaft of sun as she swung down the slope and vanished. The children's voices floated up from the creek. Cuchang still sat on his stump, now listening with his face to the sky, until a paddle rattled in a *curee-ole* and he rose, walking down the edge of the field only to stop again, as if uncertain. Amelia's voice sounded faintly telling the children to return, but they did not come for a while, refusing to accept this end to the customary swim.

Cuchang suddenly stepped off quickly through the cassava and disappeared as the children trailed back, the two boys glum, Mikme swinging her arms gaily above her head.

Paddles sounded from the creek in a slow one-two rhythm. Five minutes went by, but the village was still, the men rocking in their hammocks and the women continuing to weave small baskets, without a murmur of talk. I felt restless and went out down to the rubbish pit I had dug below the hut, and continuing without any particular aim on a hidden path over some rotten logs. The children would not follow me, as they knew this was my usual route to the creek, so I scaled the logs and reached the water without being seen. Here I removed my rope slippers and slid in. In the distance a wavy line of bubbles showed where the *curee-ole* had taken an unsteady course.

Curious, I swam slowly after them and came round a bend to see the stern of the *curee-ole* lying out of the green verge. No one was there, so I went up to the bank and sat in the sun, hearing nothing. Then laughter broke out somewhere up on the bank: Cuchang gave a throaty gurgle, but the girl was silent. They were sitting under a huge boulder, known to be a good place for a day's siesta and fishing, which stood over a little sand-spit which was above water when the creek was low. The fishing-rods were leaning against a tree and Cuchang was still taunting and pleading. Amelia's smile sounded in her voice as she said, *"Canait, Canait*—no." I now realised what I had run myself into and thought it time to go.

But I, too, was caught in the lazy voluptuousness of the village following the big haul of meat, and felt inquisitive. I reached the edge of the boulder. Amelia was sitting cross-legged in the shade, twirling the ends of her beads, but Cuchang was out of sight. His hand appeared and grasped her; she swung off her seat and disappeared back in the hollow under the rock. They were silent for a long time and, fearing they had wind of me, I walked back to the village. They were away all evening and I sensed the village knew.

Soon after I returned, Peta came over from his house and swung in through my door. He grinned.

"*Aiye*," he said in a knowing tone.

"How."

He looked all about the house, as they usually do, and

eventually sat on one of my stools. His smooth round face wore the alert innocence I had come to know from him, his brown eyes showed healthy whites, and his teeth shone as he cocked his head to one side.

"*Wapuka*—bathing?"

"*Yawaik*—yes."

"You go far?"

"The sun is not plenty in the creek that way so I sit."

"Ugh-hugh. Ugh-hugh." He pondered. An insect buzzed somewhere. His eyes were puckered, the corners of his mouth twitched with suppressed amusement. I wanted to ask if Cuchang had really gone to fish, but knew it would set him on further, so I sat down and gave him a cigarette and one of the flour bakes and said:

"Sun very hot. I think all animals asleep."

"*Yawaik*—yes," he said thoughtfully.

"What about hunting in savannahs?"

"Little bit. Little bit. Macoushi punish plenty."

"Why?"

"He shoot toucan today. He shoot toucan tomorrow. He shoot toucan next day. Only toucan!"

He sat puffing the cigarette and looking out of the window, now and then examining the bake for a while on each side before suddenly tearing off a huge chunk and eating as if he were starving, as Indians usually do. Eventually he turned to me.

"Tomorrow we go walk. I take you to small falls to find coue-ga moss."

"All right. I'll come." Before I could move he stood up to go.

"*Aqwoq. Aqwoq*—hammock," he said, and went off to his hut for a sleep. I looked through a crack in the wall of the hut and saw Cuchang coming up through the cassava, his *saloe* wet as if he had been swimming. He swung his fishing-rods and rolled along in high spirits.

"*Marouk brijeh*—no fish," he shouted to the silent village, a fact which everyone knew. He slipped behind a post and let go of his *saloe*, whipping it in the wind to dry. The children ran out to him, but he turned from them. Seeing the girl was not there they pattered off down to the creek, where there was much ostentatious splashing from Amelia. Peta was talking to Cuchang between puffs of his cigarette. The children escorted Amelia back and all was too correct for words.

In the evening the fires woke up, the women were scraping their pots and the children screaming at their pets. The incense smell of iowa gum from the firelighting wafted over the houses. In the weeks ahead there would be little to do except enjoy life; the rafters were stocked with meat and the weather was balmy. I felt this as much as the Indians, in whose ways I was now almost at one with them.

Peta came next morning as arranged and asked me if I was ready, and we wandered for half a mile and collected the moss, which Peta put in a bamboo phial. In the following days I did some repairs to my house while the village lazed. A few days later I decided to look at the farm and told the boys I wanted some of the women to go there to clean it up a bit, so Cuchang and his wife, Cassequak and his wife, Labba and two other girls, with a bunch of children, went down three days later. I walked over at midday the next day with my gun, climbed a hillock and stood behind some brambles to see the farm and who was in it. Two of the girls were stooping as they weeded, Labba was lolling under a shade, and the other pairs were not in sight. Like an Indian I stood there motionless for an hour, waiting for something to happen.

At the side of the farm which clung to the slope of the hillock, Cuchang appeared by a roundabout route and began to cut the sugar cane. It needed felling, but he did not stack it as usual, but put posts in the ground and leaned two others from them, hanging the cane leaves across them to make a shade. It was in a place invisible from the rest of the farm, but not from where I stood on the seldom-visited hillock. I was four hundred yards away and could not hear him talk, but every now and then he stopped chopping and turned as if making a remark to someone. A girl's head then came in view—not Amelia's: I was unsure whose it was.

He jerked his head as he turned each time and I knew he was only answering when she taunted him. He finished the shelter and came to the other side; they stood facing each other and his arm flashed as he grabbed her hair. She fell down on her knees and pushed him away, and he walked back to his side, swinging his head from side to side as if amused, while she stood up and looked around for many minutes. They sat, every now and then shooting glances up the hill, as if they knew someone was watching them—a common Indian precaution, even when no one is in sight. But the spell worked on me and I became so conscious of it that I left. I began to realise that they felt awkward with me living in the village, although by now accepted as one of them; the fact was that I had no woman and no one was sure, including myself, whether I wanted one. Meanwhile enjoyment rustled in every bush.

After a few days I called Mamiya, the old woman, Labba's mother. She sat on the camp step and I asked her if she could make some cassava bread for me in exchange for some wheat flour. She could not make very much she said, she was too old. I knew she would not want to lose the offer of the wheat flour and waited as she thought.

"I ask Cuchang's wife, Amelia," she said.

"I give you some flour anyway and give flour to Amelia."

She fixed her lips in a gently disapproving smile of conspiracy. Too late I realised that she thought my gift of flour to her without making a request was to buy her co-operation. This was typical, and I knew it would be useless to say anything. Words would now be mere farce. She stood up.

"When girl come I send. She make *aki*—bread."

"Good, Mamiya." We both kept a straight face until she walked away.

I smiled at the situation behind her back, and she turned and saw me. "Mmmmm," she hummed, and went on her way above the fields.

During the night I heard Mamiya's voice in suppressed but peremptory tones urging someone. In the next few days I saw Cuchang once or twice, and the other men, but they said nothing and bore no oddness in their looks. Of course, they knew as little as I did about the women's intentions and were equally uncertain about my motives. I only felt borne along in an atmosphere now thick with Mamiya's conspiratorial glances, the brush of women's feet in and out of her hut and whispers everywhere. Anything, it seemed, could happen, and most of the village apparently looked forward to an intrigue, except the men, of which I was counted as one.

Amelia came in the next few days without her usual smile and chatter. She asked if she could have a basin to make the *aki*.

"What's wrong?"

"*Waluk-nang*—I don't know."

I gave her the basin, but held it; she gripped it, then tugged it away. Mamiya has made an impression, I thought, and I called her back.

"You put basin here. I don't want *aki* any more," I said. She gave me a half-surprised look and walked briskly back to Mamiya's house, probably to say I was not ready to have it made.

Two days passed. Cuchang did not go about with his wife and would not come to see me. The old woman eventually arrived with her basin for the flour I had promised. She looked about the hut.

"Where is the *aki*?"

"Girl did not make," I said. "Girl is vexed. I no want anyone around vexed."

Mamiya frowned.

"You lie." She looked all over the hut for the *aki*.

"No." I said. She left in a hurry and spoke sharply to the children hanging round the door, then popped her head out in a minute and called three girls. I could hear her voice raised for some minutes as she preached to them.

The girls would not heed Mamiya and did not speak to me for several days. There was an undecided mood in the village until Peta and Labba arrived one morning with studied casualness.

Peta sat on the step. "All girls want to work for you," he said. "This man wife, this man wife, all girl."

"Work in the farm?" I asked. He raised his eyebrows.

"Anything, anything; do work, little bit work, you give them cloth make dress," he said airily.

"How many?"

"Four."

"Too much, four! If work in farm, good."

"Everything, work. Clean place, do little bit work."

"No," I said. "Two work farm. Two work here." They ceased being serious and Labba turned.

"Good *yapung*," he said. "You make book." I had a book in which I used to scribble who worked for me and the time spent: when I handed out cloth and other things at the end of three months or so the book was consulted, and as long as I put a circle or a cross in the book all was regular. Now they all came, the children, the women, the men and Misterisaac. I brought out the book and all eyes fastened on it in deep silence. I ran through all the names in the list to reassure them.

"Labba, Peta, Mamiya, Misterisaac, Cuchang, Cassequak . . . Mikme—for pulling the weeds. Amelia, Powice . . ." Two other girls were on the list, whose names were seldom used and whom I called simply *ourishang*, which means girl. Their names appeared as marks by which I could distinguish them.

Powice was the smartest of them. She might have been Peta's sister from her moon face, though her eyes slanted more than his did and she wore a perpetual, bewitching smile. Below she was stocky and tough, a tomboy with old beads swinging carelessly, but with fine breasts.

"Yapung, who work farm, who work here?" she asked.

"Anyone."

"I can cook rice," she stated.

"No." I said. I preferred to cook my own food.

"*Achee*—make fire," she suggested.

"Powice, you put two in farm, two here. This way you work. Look, two work in farm, two here. One bring water from creek in morning when sun is up, same one wash my clothes. Next one come soon morning, before sun awake, before sun at all awake must come and make fire to heat water in this." I pointed to an old butter tin from whose ends I had fixed wire handles to make a pan. "Put this on fire to heat water." I drummed in these instructions firmly to settle the business finally.

To make the situation sufficiently intriguing I closed and locked the back door out of the kitchen lean-to, as I usually did at night, but left my front door open and slung my hammock Indian-style about six inches off the ground in front of the inner door into the kitchen. Whoever came in the early morning would have to wake me to pass to the fireplace. But at the first dawn no one came to make the fire. Later, after sun-up, Powice came with water and took some clothes to wash in the creek. She had taken the second duty so Amelia, Cuchang's wife, had been forced into the embarrassing first place and had shirked at the last minute; convinced, despite all I could do, that I had tried to buy her through Mamiya.

It went on like this for three days, Powice coming each morning and departing with a load of clothes without a word, and the other two working on the farm. Then one morning I awoke to the sound of the fire crackling and saw a figure through the cracks of the partition in the kitchen. It was one of the *ourishangs* who was supposed to be working on the farm: she must have noticed that no one was coming early and come herself. She could only have passed me without waking me by hitching up her beads and jumping my hammock, which must have taken time to achieve. Every minute she turned quickly to see if I was moving. Finally I turned and the rope squeaked.

"Yapung," she said, "me *canega apuk*—me make fire."

"Good," I said. She had been the conscientious one and I let her be.

"When you finish, take some bakes, open the door at the back and you can go," I added.

I listened to her footsteps padding away among the houses. A door swished open and I heard Amelia's voice.

"You go *yapung banabu*. You *canega apuk*. You go farm."
Amelia saw no reason for this girl to usurp her rights, although
she was not availing herself of them.

"Well, yapung punish. Three mornings punish. No one
light fire." I was amused at the sudden discovery that I had
suffered lack of attention when for two years I had made my
own fire and hauled my own water.

"I go make fire," continued the *ourishang*, "every morning."

"You cannot. You work farm. You stay farm." The talking continued and other girls collected to hear the case. Eventually Mamiya told them all to go back to sleep and there was
silence.

That morning, after this sudden turn of jealousy, Cuchang
was walking round, frowning and looking about distractedly.
Although accustomed, like the other men, to the women being
discreetly shared, he did not like the prospect of his wife coming to my hut. I called to him, "Cuchang, come."

He ran across and sat on the stool I offered.

"Cuchang, plenty trouble. *Ourishang* quarrel, no work."
I pulled out the book. "Look, some *ourishang* work." I pointed
to the straight lines in front of some names for their days of
work. "Others no work at all." He saw a row of zeros. "Look,
Powice work. But Amelia." He was now prepared to hear his
wife's name. "Amelia no work, no work, no work." I ran my
finger along the zeros. "Three week time I give them pong-
cloth. Look Amelia no work."

"You work." I pointed to his name and the row of strokes
for the days he had been out prospecting with me. "You work
good. You get something good. A *saloe* and other things, bigger
things."

"Good," said Cuchang. "What you give me now?"

"Well, not time yet. I give you now then all man will
want."

"No, other not want."

"I give *saloe* now all men see. Want sure."

208

He thought. *"Pyala*—shot. Powder?" He knew he could hide such things easily.

I agreed and produced a flask of powder, half of which I poured in an empty flask. "You get your flask, your *baggi* for shot." I said. Cuchang hurried away and returned wearing an old pair of khaki shorts I had given him, in the pocket of which he could conceal the powder and shot. He was slow in asking favours but smartened up when offered them. When he had hidden the goods I showed him the book again, by this time feeling that I was handling the business as subtly as they would.

"Ourishang, one, two, three, four, I put scratch," I said, "no work, no good," and put a line through all of them, including Amelia, without mentioning her name. They would not work here again. Cuchang could not imagine that I was trying to buy his wife by giving him gifts: we were good friends again.

"All girl lazy, all girl lazy," he said. "One hour time they work. I go see."

But I did not let him go and we sat outside the hut all day, talking and smoking, when Peta and Labba joined us to form a stag party, criticising the women with much laughter. Amelia and the other girls passed to and fro at a distance, noting this new camaraderie. The small circle sat for hours discussing everything under the sun—hunting, fishing, but always coming back to the subject of women. We split up in the evening in good spirits.

Next morning Amelia came, but after the sun had woken, and with Mikme and the two little boys. She squeezed under my hammock and lit the fire. I played 'possum and the only sufferer was the old butter tin, which boiled dry. Later I called Peta, not Cuchang.

"Soon morning Peta who came make fire?"

Peta turned back and shouted at the village—"Which girl make *yapung* fire?"

Amelia answered that she had. I showed Peta the inside of the hut. "Plenty little feet in sand. How many people came

209

here?" I pretended to be vexed and said I did not want children in my hut at all. This had been a standing order and Peta agreed that it was bad. I knew he would stop it. At night I heard much talk about the children.

Next morning Amelia came, very early, long before dawn: I heard a creak of the floor and smelt her. I could not see, but knew she was standing by the hammock looking down at me, waiting to creep under, convinced I would snatch at her. Eventually she eased herself under, walked a few steps and turned, walked and turned again; but I was as still and quiet as if dead to the world. She hopped down into the kitchen and soon had the fire burning. Then I moved and she played with the fire, waiting for sun-up before leaving.

"Amelia," I called softly. She did not answer. "When you finish, open door near fire and you can go."

"*Aiye?*"

"When you finish you can go."

She put the water on, looked around, opened the door and went.

For a week running she came as regular as clockwork. Once or twice she even shook the hammock purposely, hopped over and went to the kitchen. I said nothing. It was now quite clear that I was not buying the women, and there was no mystery left in making my fire. But, I wondered, had I not gone too far in the interests of fair play? Now it seemed impossible for me to carry on a minor intrigue as the other men did: I had put myself out in the cold.

One morning it was drizzling hard and Amelia came through the rain. She twitched the hammock again and hopped over, and I caught the usual vision of the beads rising and falling swiftly and a length of brown thigh. I knew the beads were fixed in such a way that a direct pull would not remove them: they were fastened so that an end of the string is tucked in and only that end will release them. But I knew the exact cord to pull. As she passed I called, "*Aiye.*" She stopped and I pulled the cord. The beads fell on the floor. Amelia jumped a yard back to the wall and stood facing me, with her legs crossed and her hands flat down the wall at her sides. I saw that the Indians believe in all respects what I had noticed with the Macoushi, that hair on the body should be completely shaved off: she was perfectly smooth.

She was smiling, and I called her softly, *"Oitka, oitka."*

"Mamiya, Mamiya awake. Mamiya come."

"No, *oitka.*"

She stood there for a minute. "All right," I said, "you *canega apuk.*"

"Canait, canait—no." She wanted the beads.

"No. You *canega apuk.* I keep this." I reached down and took the beads.

"Mamiya awake," she said, raising her voice slightly to attract attention. I threw the beads at her and she put them on and stepped down into the kitchen. After making the fire she left as usual, in a good humour. When Powice came later with the water I could tell from her vexed expression that she had been outside the hut, had heard something of the affair and was jealous of Amelia. It was becoming the ambition of all the girls to flirt with me and the men seemed agreeable: Mamiya's plan that I should be put at ease had become village policy; I wondered who would be the first to act on it.

Powice came next morning with the water as usual. When she had put it in the kitchen she turned.

"Yapung, me go in *curee-ole,*" she whispered. "Me go under big stone."

"Icheh warawak—want man?" I asked since there could be no other reason for going to the well-known spot.

In the morning there was no sign of Powice and I was sure she had gone to the stone, so I took my hidden trail past the rubbish pit and over the logs down to the creek. I stood on top of the stone and she was sitting in the shade below. Faced with the prospect before me, I became disconcerted: the game was getting a little hot. I climbed down slowly and sat down. She did not look at me, but scanned the surrounding bushes and the creek in the usual manner, and breathing quickly, asked me where this person and that person was, running through every adult's name. I told her as far as I knew what they all were doing. She stood up and composed her face, leaning against the rock, relaxed but silent. "Your husband vex," I said, and began to play with the ends of her beads. She looked at me and laughed, an ingenuous giggle, without malice. To play with a girl's beads is the height of intimacy and I felt I must go on. "Come," I said, "sit down."

"No." She laughed. I rose to my feet. She was under five feet while I am nearer six. I was puzzled: how did she expect the next moves to be carried out? Perhaps, I thought, the Indians have their own peculiar manner of conducting themselves on these occasions. I held her by the waist and hooked the cord of her beads in my little finger. She said nothing but pressed my hand softly; I pulled the cord and she stood there, again motionless, without expression. "You want me?" I asked.

"I don't know," she said. At least this seemed normal.

Suddenly she smiled and pushed her face under mine.

"*Yawaik*—yes," she said, as if to indicate that I was slow on the uptake.

"Sit down then."

"No."

"You sit down. People pass, see, sit down." I held her hand but she would not move. This went on for an hour, both of us standing and arguing softly. Eventually I suggested that she should return to the village.

"No. You go first," she said. I hooked the beads back on her and we left in turn. I puzzled over the scene for the whole afternoon. Then it flashed on me—she merely wanted to draw level with the other girl and be seen by me as I had seen Amelia, nothing more. It seemed that Powice was forward but not completely abandoned.

I saw Powice moving about the village that evening as if nothing had happened, and it was clear that none of the others knew about it. Eventually the village went to sleep and I turned into my hammock. Then about midnight I awoke to hear soft footsteps. It was Powice, and she had come for good this time.

She lay impassively for about an hour, but when I made a move she sank her nails into my back and called, "*Icheh, icheh*—quick, quick." She wanted me to stay with her, and I began to realize why the couples who went off together stayed for so many hours: it is the Indian custom to spend anything up to six hours together. With Powice the only sign of passion was when she took my index finger and chewed it. The Indians do not kiss and rarely embrace. As dawn approached, I told her the others would be moving soon and she went.

When she came on the following mornings with water she gave no sign of our relationship. Her smile was back in place but when I asked each time if she would come in the night she said that she did not know. Sometimes I took her hand but she loosed it at once, and it was soon apparent that our affair of that night was now closed, without leaving a ripple or touching her perpetual smile, although we talked together often; which Amelia began to notice.

Then Amelia came one morning and began to address me, then paused. "Come," I said, "sit down."

"No," she said, and remained standing at the end of my hammock.

"What's wrong?"

"You wanting other *ourishang*." She could not have known anything, but I knew she meant Powice.

"*Canait*—no, no good, no good." It was necessary to deprecate in the Indian fashion.

"Sometime you want me? You want me, me stay. Bring me *aqwoq*, my hammock, put this house." Amelia was a different kind of girl from Powice, and the homebuilding instinct was clearly apparent. This was going too far and would have upset the entire village.

"No, you wait one moon, two moon, bring hammock."

"Long time," she said.

"No, you come one hour two hour now. One moon bring hammock."

She caught the drift of this proposition but wanted to be

213

sure of the permanency of the future arrangement. I was to give her two lengths of cloth; when I went back to the frontier I was to fetch other things.

"Sometime, sometime," I said as diplomatically as possible.

In a few days, after some preliminary sitting on the edge of my hammock, she rolled in as Powice had done. She seemed more content at the amount of time I spent with her, but she insisted on coming to me every day. As with Powice there was little passion, until one night it was clear that she felt more than mere submissiveness. Having achieved this satisfaction, that night marked the end of the relationship; not only did she stop coming to my hammock, but she stopped working for me altogether. The motives behind the actions of Powice and Amelia at that time have remained a mystery to me to this day, but perhaps they also had no clear idea of them. At least I had discovered that the Indian control over their emotions goes to great lengths.

Soon after this time of love-making, which was accentuated because of the amount of meat the village had stored, the cotton trees were in full bloom at the top of the fields, standing in a clean clump by themselves. The children were often warned not to play among them. The chief amusement of the children is to cut down small trees, rather than to climb them, but they kept away from the cotton trees and the women were careful to weed out small bushes from about them. Cotton was the chosen kingdom of Misterisaac who, although foolish in other ways, had become the master weaver of the village.

The cotton stood light green against the darker jungle, about the height of plum trees, the blooms bursting balls of white, the strands streaming in the breeze. Misterisaac moved about them, looking over the blooms, and one day took up the hill a small *warishi* which he filled with the cotton balls to take down to the village, where he wandered about until he had found a huge tray in the *aki* house. A small boy cleaned it for him and the brooms were spread in the sun for a few hours.

Meanwhile, the others were busy refurbishing the houses, some out collecting leaves and poles, others clambering up the long supports from the roofs which are left as permanent ladders used for repairs. The men lay on the roofs and the women stood inside the houses, looking for the sun through cracks and directing the men by shouts.

Misterisaac grinned when I came over, and asked if he could borrow my scissors to cut out the cotton seeds, normally a laborious job of picking. So we sat for a time cutting out the white cotton, removing the stems, seeds and other unwanted matter; by handling, the cotton was turning from snowy white to brown. The Indians never have any white cloth: they will make a hammock starting with white cotton and by the time it is finished it is brown, being further stained a rich nut colour by the smoke of the fires. When we had cut out the cotton we took it into his house out of the wind and spread it on the spacious floor. Misterisaac had one of the bigger houses, about forty feet by twenty, with the roof about eighteen feet above, so that it was cool and roomy, better in fact than many houses in the tropics.

When he went to find his weaving sticks, the children crowded round as usual and tumbled the cotton so that it went a darker shade of brown. He came back and started teasing out the cotton in long strands with both hands together so that the strand passed from his finger-tips between the balls of his palms, scuffling the cotton there with a quick motion and half spinning it. With a stick he began coiling the strands until he had a large loose spool of rough strand; he then put a spindle between his toes and held another in his left hand, so that the cotton from the spindle in his toes came to the other in his hand, which he turned and drew in sweeps to thin out the strands into thread without breaking it. All this while a small boy stood motionless watching him, intrigued and likely to become a pupil. In this way by natural selection of apprenticeship, the children choose their crafts in the village circle. I was struck by the scene as an example of how men would wish to manage their industry, where individual fascination and skill are paramount, where time and money do not enter to strangle and deform such qualities.

Misterisaac then put the full spindle in his toes and spun the cotton once more, this time taking a small length and gradually drawing it out, spinning with the palms of his hands. The reel in his toes swung one way, then the other, as his palms worked, also one way and the other, but in opposite time. So the rhythm stretched and spun the threads. Sometimes the thin thread burst and Misterisaac joined it as Amelia had done when she made the fishing lines, by fraying the ends and merely laying them together and spinning again. This whole procedure produced one thread, and had to be repeated many times to produce a number of threads which were then run together to make a strong line for weaving. The finished line, although so simply made, was strong and even, so that I could not break it by a direct pull, although it was easily weakened by giving a slight twist and unloosing the threads from each other.

He was working to weave a child's hammock to replace an old one which would now be unwoven for thread to patch any torn hammock in the village, a task which would be under Mamiya's supervision. He set up the frame of the hammock outside, two poles about five feet long facing each other, suspended from uprights in the ground behind each, and from the centre of one pole drew a cotton cord to the centre of the other to hold the poles in the air and start the weaving. On either side of the centre cord, he wound about a hundred others parallel to it and around the poles at either end. Where the cords passed around the poles he made eyes and the size of the hammock in length and breath was now fixed by the warp. Then he began interlacing the woof across the warp, using only his fingers which worked up and down speedily. He wove another warp lengthwise crossing the woof on alternate sides from the first warp, then another woof crossing the two warps and knotted like a fishing net, making a soft, strong and pretty cloth. The ends were strengthened with extra weaving and the loops removed from the poles.

He made a thick ring through the loops in place of the

poles with cotton taken round on itself in the manner of a sailor's grommet or strop. From the strops the hammock was suspended and that completed the job, except for stretching it between two whippy saplings stuck in the ground, leaning away from each other.

The others went on with their work as well, polishing the gourds and cutting out new ones, weaving baskets, repairing the houses, including mine; the time was drawing on to the next feast, but this time our village was going as the guest of another in the plains. This had been planned towards the end of the last feast and there was less anxiety as the villagers knew they would be free from the care of entertaining others. However, a good deal of cassili was made to set the celebrations going when the time came. So the year had come round, arranged in a cycle full of variety, of hunting, love-making, sowing and reaping, travelling to new districts and redecorating the home. Life may be poor for the Indian, but it is not dull.

The time had come when the village was expecting men to come from the frontier to accompany us to the plains, and one morning, when Labba and Peta were swimming in the creek, they heard the knock of *curee-ole* paddles. They shouted that a boat was coming and the whole village dropped everything and ran in a crowd to the top of the fields where they could see a stretch of the creek. Everyone was silent, listening to count the paddle beats, which soon made it clear that two paddlers were coming. Mamiya came across to me hopping on her toes like a child, holding up the skirt of a dress she had made from my cloth.

"*Kapung yabu. Kapung yabu*—Indians coming from plains," she whispered excitedly.

"Good."

She turned and began ordering the girls about: they must get the big pot from the *aki* house and put it out on the sand with fresh cassava bread. Powice, Amelia and two other girls ran over to my house and stood in an expectant line, much in the way they had welcomed me when I first arrived. After a long wait Peta and Labba came up from the landing stage with the visitors. One was thick-set, wearing khaki trousers, but naked, like an Indian, from the waist up. He was a half-breed, unusually fair, with a pleasant face but thicker lips than an Indian, a sign of his part Brazilian blood, and small eyes. His hair, though, was truly Indian: straight, black and cut sharply around his head. He also wore bead wrist bands of the Akowayo and a twine necklace with a small nut at the end. The other was smaller and with less air to him, a boy whom the older man dominated.

The burly one was laughing and talking loudly in a strangely uncouth frontier manner compared with the delicate way of the hills. "*Ce passa, ce passa,*" he was saying in bad Spanish. Powice turned. "A little Brazilian." "Yes," I said, "maybe he is Brazilian and Akowayo mixed."

"No good. Kapung no good," the girls murmured. But he did not look such a bad fellow.

They came to the middle of the village square beside the pots and Mamiya called them to eat, "*Sileh, sileh, aki atai.*" The visitors pulled their pants up and squatted, the Indian habit dropping on them like a cloak, concealing the bigger one's boastfulness as he dug his bread in the pot and smeared his fingers on his chest. They ate for some time and were obviously hungry after a long journey; afterwards they sat round a huge fire with the men, talking late, but slept in an open shelter built for them, as it was not considered correct for them to board in any of the houses. The whole village got ready to move the next morning, asking many questions of the strangers, chiefly how much food there was in the host village. They said there was plenty and the others had brought old pickle barrels from the frontier to store a great amount of cassili.

Next morning I told Peta that all the doors should be secured and that valuables such as arrow-heads, cloth, hammocks and spare bows could be put in my house, which had a padlock. A great amount of packing went on in my arsenal while I washed in the creek and sharpened my knife in the sand. When I returned I could not get through the door: in their excitement they had stacked the place with black pots, evil-smelling hunks of meat, firewood, iowa gum and *aki*. I told Labba to clear it out, leaving only vital things. The meat was put back in the rafters of the houses except for that of the hogs we had shot, which were to supply us on the trip. The women carried everything, leaving the men free. Powice took my hammock and, like the other men, I walked around with small things, stuffing them in any *warishi* with room to spare. The women also take their children, so they were to bear the brunt of this trip. The men stood about with their weapons, their headbands and bright clean *saloes*, smoking tobacco which I handed out.

Finally we told them to get down to the boats and Mamiya gathered all the children. The men took centre seats with Peta, Labba and Cassequak steering the largest boats. The women paddled all the way to the first falls, a few miles down from the village, where the men sank the boats in the usual way and from where we spread out in a long file, more than twenty of us, and set off through the jungle: a bright, chattering column with the men in front and the women with the children behind. The trail was dry and pleasant walking, but there was little to shoot, only toucans which Peta had so derisively listed as the Macoushi diet when the land was dry. The heat became more trying and the men chose trails leading through as many creeks as possible, through which the whole village paddled and stopped sometimes to bathe. The march seemed endless, and after seven days of it the pace began to tell on the heavily laden women. Each night the camp found itself in a circle without any particular order, sometimes on the edge of great savannahs like the pampas, which began like an endless stretching of the earth to draw down the lofty jungle to small patches, then to mere bushes and thorns. Then the plains would give way to steep mountains over which we straggled and toiled. The creeks and rivers flowed faster as we drew near to the destination near the watershed of the Ireng River, where they were not navigable by canoe.

We were entering the rich diamond lands best known to prospectors, and passed many of their workings: crumbling

219

pits, sheds and trails which wound in and out of them in such a way that the men knew they had been made by "pirate" buyers circulating in their business. We hurried on, although I knew that I could spend ten years thereabouts and keep finding new diamond deposits, as the area is so vast it has hardly been touched. The men were not concerned about the women and children, as it was customary for a young girl runner to catch up should there be any reason for a halt. But all went well and the children kept the pace.

As we approached the savannah where the feast was to be held, the men ran on down the hills, every so often, giving the piercing Indian call I had first heard at the village party. At the foot of the last rise we squatted down and waited for the women to close up. My skin streamed with sweat but I noticed, as often before, that the Indians did not perspire so copiously and merely became oily. After an hour the women plodded up, their hair plastered down their backs, straining at the *warishi* straps round their foreheads, Mamiya, who was leading with a full load, asking why we were so lazy. We said we were waiting for her and the other women.

"Get up. Go. Go," she said sharply and hustled us on. Mamiya had gradually taken her husband's position as the senior member of the village and her words carried weight: without a murmur the men strode ahead. My gun felt heavy and I sympathised with the younger women behind. That night we ate most of our food to lighten the weight of the *warishis* for the final lap, and the scraps left were packed in one *warishi*. Next morning we set off again, the men yelling as before. Amelia was close behind carrying Mikme as well as her *warishi* and at every few steps I heard her saying to herself "*Ineh paojee, ineh paojee*—it's heavy." I looked round at her and her lips curled down and trembled with the effort. After half an hour I turned again and told her to give me Mikme, but she walked past me.

I was not surprised, as the Indians rarely respond at once, so I walked behind her for a while and then swung her round by her shoulder and told her again. She smiled and unloosed

Mikme from the sling for me to take. Mikme started to cry and Mamiya remarked that she now felt too high in the air because of my height. Soon I was aching, and muscles I did not know existed called for rest. Just as I was about to sit down we saw two men running across the plain towards us shouting greetings, their teeth stained red from drinking cassili. We knew the party had started.

The feast was being held at the crossing of several trails and not, as usual, in a village. It had been organised by an old Macoushi couple, well known in the mountains, whose house stood alone in the scrub on the great plain. He was a renowned hunter with many strings of boar's teeth, and he and his wife had been astute enough to have gathered a modest wealth from the prospectors, adventurers and wastrels who passed by their door. Towards their house we now walked with the messengers and heard the deep beat of drums from two miles off in time to the chant of at least fifty voices, singing in much the same strain as that of most Indian songs. As we approached we could see that a small village of palm shelters had sprung up around a large clearing, lit by a blazing fire in whose leaping light danced, ran and strolled dozens of people of many tribes, some of mixed blood. There must have been nearly two hundred all told, each party based on its small camp but roaming about, some with furtive intentions towards the girls, others filled merely with goodwill, but all gay from cassili. The married women formed a solid committee, inquiring chiefly who were the unmarried males in order to fulfil their usual duty as matchmakers. Around the dancing ring stood many barrels, filled with cassili, which must have cost a great effort to roll the two days' journey from the nearest Brazilian trading post. On barbecues between them hung dozens of carcasses, spluttering over their individual fires—enough to gorge all the feasters for more than a week. In the same outer ring also lay fifteen or twenty canoes filled with cassili which tossed and splashed over the gunwales from the constant dipping of gourds. This gathering of Arawaks, Akowayos, Macoushi, Patamona, Wai-wai and half-breeds was the largest I had seen in the hills. The Patamona contingent were our party of twenty or so and about fifteen others, some of them from the village which had visited us at the previous feast. The noise was intense, with at least four drums of deer-skin going continuously, the largest keeping the basic beat and the others improvising. The drums were wide and shallow, the bodies neatly built from bamboo, and were beaten with sticks. A Macoushi youth was playing a fiddle of his own design, a pear-shaped block of wood cunningly burned hollow, with a single string from the point to the base supported on two bridges. He was able to vary the notes by the bow alone, but I could not get close enough to see how this was managed.

As soon as we came into the firelight, the women unloaded, rolled up their hair and began cutting fronds for a shelter, while Macoushi ran up with huge *gubis* of liquor. Mine held at least a gallon, but I thought I should change into my best clothes before drinking, to keep up with the others, some of whom wore magnificent costumes of heavy beading, feathers and leaf hats, as the villagers had done the last time. A few of the girls were dressed in cloth bought from prospectors. I left the crowd for a few moments and changed behind the bushes. When I returned I sipped my cassili slowly: it was strong and thick and I hoped for some of the special cassili which is kept hidden at such feasts for favoured guests. Peta was already half through his *gubi* and those waiting on us soon noticed that I was slow with mine. For a moment our attention was diverted by Misterisaac, who had changed into his finery and now leaped into the ring and capered about with a fatuous grin, for a few minutes leading the dance with a fantastic tattoo of steps. He laughed at everyone and was immediately accepted as the clown of the feast.

Peta and I wandered through the crowd, leaving Powice and Amelia watching the dance. The Macoushi asked me if I did not like the cassili and I asked for "*waki cassili*—the good wine." At once the old hunter appeared. "Come," he said, and led me into his house, which was swept clean, filled with benches of cassava bread and many beads hanging from the walls; from the rafters were strung the heads and antlers of some of the old man's kills, a rare custom among Indians. He had cured his trophies in the sun and they seemed reasonably well preserved. I sat on a small stool and his wife, who sat at one end of the hut, dug in the sand under her hammock and produced two glass bottles corked with leaves, which she held up to the light for me to see the clear liquid and then pressed to my chest. "Hide them," she said, "the others should not see or all will want it." I thanked her and crept out the back way.

Peta saw me and came splashing along with his gourd. He asked what I had and, when I told him, laughed and put his hand on my shoulder and made off with me towards the bushes. Powice saw us and ran up. Peta chased her away, saying we did not want *ourishangs* with us, but I said there would be enough for her as well, so he called her back. We sat in the bushes and finished the two bottles in a few minutes: the cassili was as smooth as an ordinary white table wine with a fine, slightly sweet taste, and the effect, I knew, would be as perfect as the taste. This cassili is taken from the normal brew after being allowed to settle in gourds for a week or two, when the ground cassava had settled and a foam has formed on the surface. The foam is removed and the clear liquid ladled into another gourd. Fresh cassava is taken, grated, squeezed and added, without colouring matter, to continue the fermentation. After a few weeks the cassava "sets." The Indians judge this by tasting frequently choosing the moment when the bitterness gives way to a slight sweetness. Then it is again decanted into clean gourds and some sweet fruit juice is added, commonly from the ripe balata plum. This is the final flavouring and the wine is then bottled in small gourds or, near the frontier, in glass bottles.

Another drink they had at this feast was the famous *pywari*, which looks and tastes like bitter malt beer but is the colour of stout. This is made from sweet potatoes in much the same way as the best cassili. There was not much of this, as the bitter taste is favoured only as an occasional contrast to the cassili. A third drink was a refinement of the *pywari*, much stronger, with the same sleep-making effect as strong ale.

No one slept and the excitement continued at full pace through the next day to the night, many couples sneaking off into the dark and returning to drink again and find new partners. Laughter and shouting pierced the steady rhythm of the chant, the stamping feet and the booming drums. Some of the younger braves joined in gangs and walked drunkenly through others' camps, breaking down the walls and marching on, with only slight annoyance from the inmates to check them. The older men and women sat more quietly, talking of the hunting and the likely marriages. On the third morning I went back to the house and found the old Macoushi couple inside, but the house quite bare: they had called their young men and taken all their possessions to the bush and buried them there for safety. But the bottles remained, coming up from the underground bar, and I collected two more.

That morning many slept through the noise, including myself, Peta, Labba and also Amou, who had been missing most of the time on some private adventure. Men lay about in the sand where they had fallen. Others were laced round trees; only needing a nudge and the word *cassili* in their ears to awaken them with a jolt and a laugh to start drinking again. Once more I was amazed by their stamina in dancing sometimes for seventy or eighty hours without stopping except to eat and drink excessively. Their habit of leaving long intervals of hunting between these bouts of drinking, and the exercise of dancing, no doubt partly accounts for their fitness despite these debauches. Also the effect of cassili seems to reach saturation point in about forty-eight hours, after which one is left in a maniac state without further stupefaction. I began to cool down and spent most of the afternoon with the old Macoushi hosts, partly to pay them respect on behalf of the party I was with.

The old man spoke a little English which he took pride in, and we sat talking and drinking the dark *pywari* as a cocktail before supper. Towards sundown I looked through the door at the crowd and saw an old man stepping slowly and as straight as he could towards the house, using a long stave to clear the way. He wore nothing except a *saloe* and a string of beads around his neck, his upper lip bulging with *couega*. He looked only at our host, asking how he was, speaking through his teeth in a form of groan, which is considered the polite form of address on meeting, and indicating by his manner that he waited for an introduction to me. I could see from the faint tattoo lines above and parallel to his eyebrows that he was a Macoushi.

"Come, *amako*," said the hunter. "Cassili." The old man held on to his stick, turned around, turned back, tightened his *saloe* and sank by degrees on to his thin haunches and began to sip the proffered *pywari*. I asked him where he came from and he turned his head slowly to me, and raised his arm. "*Moujeeee*," he whined—"Far."

"*Nai*—where?" I asked.

"Ireng."

"Plenty Brazilian there," I said, thinking of the prospectors.

"No," he said, "far, very far, top Ireng."

I attended more carefully and my prospector's instinct was aroused. The headwaters of the Ireng were untapped, reputedly rich but hard to reach. Then I noticed that among the beads round his neck was a string on the end of which was some black wax: embedded there, half concealed, I saw that a diamond gleamed. It appeared to be about two carats and of flawless light green; worth I estimated no less than £100. I looked at the stone and then at the old man and realised what Smiler must have felt whenever he met a prospector with stones. Somehow I must bargain with the old man and buy this stone, I thought. I began to ask him how prospection was in his area. He groaned between his teeth, croaking lazily, "Sometime good, sometime bad," giving nothing away. He paused.

"Ireng good place."

"You got good place?"

"No, but good place Ireng." He had taken me round in a circle, but, it seemed, for a purpose. He was interested in my knife and asked if I had more. I lied and said I had.

"I give you something, you give me something," I said.

The old men both chortled.

"How many people you bring with you?" I asked.

"Me bring? Me bring nobody," he said mildly.

"You walk. Alone. Nobody?"

The old hunter began to hiss and giggle.

"Yapung, he lie," he said at last.

The old man started to point out his party through the door. His wife, his son and then his daughter. I looked at her again: reddened lips, a well-curved figure and a honey skin. She would have been reckoned attractive anywhere and was quite exceptional for a mountain Indian. I asked him again to make sure.

"Yes, me girl," he hummed with a note of pride. I was not interested any longer and thought again of the diamond at his neck. I asked him when he would be going back, but he only said, "Sometime, sometime." Again the pause, and then he asked me what I was doing. I was equally vague and made out that I had no settled place but wandered around. I could see his mind was working. In a little while he started again. "Ireng good place. You come Ireng." I did not bite.

I lifted the stone from his chest, gave it a glance.

"You got little diamond, no good," I said and slung the stone back on his chest. I half-hoped it would fall out of the wax.

"Yes, me find."

He told me he was bathing one day in the creek, using an old *gubi* to splash water over his head. He had dipped the *gubi* and caught some sand and the diamond lay there shining. It sounded a tall story. But he would not say whereabouts he lived, and I knew it could be anywhere among a tangle of valleys and steep mountains. I sat until the small hours with him, knowing he was not uninterested in me and wondering how we could reach an understanding. Then the girl came and called for her father to come and sleep.

"No," I said, "old man stay. He drink with me. Good friends."

"Yes," echoed the old man, "good friends."

I called the girl in for a drink and she came, looking even better at night, despite her dress of Western cloth. Just as she sat down I saw Labba, Amou and Amelia coming in search for me. Labba was ahead and I deliberately turned my back on him: he took the hint and led the rest straight past the door. Then the girl squatted, pulled up her dress and hooked it above her bead skirt which she was wearing underneath. It was particularly long and heavy, of new beads, and I realised both that the old man had been doing well and that she was unmarried.

Sometimes the vigil became too much and I nodded, then thought of the diamond and jerked myself awake, to hear the old man droning on about nothing. The next day I intended to offer everything I had in exchange for it. I had got myself into an irresponsible and uninhibited mood like the rest, and felt no urge to come out of it in a hurry. We started to drink again, of the good cassili, and I suggested we collect his family to drink it outside in the bush. He was keen for me to come and prospect with him, but I pointed out the problem of living where I was and the difficulty of leaving the village. I told him I could not leave the others as I was one of them, and that, in any case, it might mean a lone journey of up to a fortnight to reach his place.

Once or twice the girl and I went off to dance and that next night all of us became good friends until, in a fit of generosity I gave him my bowie knife. He asked what I wanted in exchange and I said his beads, not meaning the diamond, although I still intended to buy it. But he was now in such a state that the beads apparently meant more than the stone: he had worked hard for the beads, he said, whereas he had picked up the diamond for nothing. It took some persuading to make him keep it, and some forbearance to refuse it. By this time I could see that he genuinely put little value on the stone, even allowing for the effects of the *cassili* and the festivity, but somehow I had lost interest in it, once more thinking of prospecting and the wealth I could get by now, after thorough apprenticeship in the jungle, and thinking also of the girl, whom I had found a good companion.

When I returned to Mamiya and the others, now packing to go, they gave me searching glances. Mamiya was upset and I dragged out of her the general suspicion that I intended to bring the Macoushi girl back to the village. I put their minds at ease, but I could see that they all were now keen to get home and restore to their lives the peace and independence of the hills. The prospect of my romance would have disturbed it and I was glad I had not become further entangled. Peta, Labba and I eventually set off down the trail, drinking and waving goodbye to the old man and his daughter. He was calling "You come in two weeks," forlornly echoed by her: "You come, *amako*, you come." I did not trust myself to speak and with one last wave, went on with the other two on each side of me, telling me I would forget all about it once we were on trail.

Soon the little column was straggling across the immense plain, travelling easily, and leaving behind a few spidery columns of smoke among the tattered shelters and the rapidly thinning crowd. My only token was a knife from the Macoushi host with a deer antler handle, which he had pressed in my hand in a hurried farewell with the advice that I would be sure one day to visit the old man and his daughter and find plenty of diamonds there.

On the slow walk back, the villagers were like a people released, relaxed from the annual bout, free to live afresh. The girls were admiring the birds flashing about in the trees. Powice stopped us all by a pool to watch the fish darting about and I suggested we should see what we could catch. While some went a short distance to gather fish-stunning herbs, I noticed Amelia collecting stones as I had seen the women do before. One she popped in her mouth, saying it was nice and smooth. In a few minutes the others returned with some of the bark used to drug the water and so catch fish, but few fish were affected by the weed and only half a dozen came to the surface. Most of them were good eating, but one I noticed was a fish I had seen before, which the prospectors call the smoke-fish.

It is a member of the family of the hassar, a highly prized table delicacy in South America, about six inches long, weighing about half a pound, the scales each forming a complete collar around it, fitting into each other like a flexible hose and the head unusually hard. The smoke-fish has a similar scale formation although not so pronounced. The mouth is rounded as if the fish was sighing O, breathing slowly in and out when it is taken from the water. I amused the Indians by putting a cigarette in its mouth, telling them that it was a smoker. The smoke-fish drew a breath, drawing in the smoke, then puffed, the smoke coming out in a perfect cone—a joke perfectly suiting their sense of humour. I could visualise one of them performing the same trick on other Indians and being regarded as a witty fellow. But his audience would be most interested, not in the performance but how he had discovered that it could be done. We put the smoke-fish back in the pool and picked up our *warishis*, after this typical interlude in the Indian day.

CHAPTER FOURTEEN
The Americans

DURING the next two days some of the children began to complain of dysentery from the cassili which they had been allowed to drink. This is not an uncommon effect from a small amount of cassili, and this time the women were sent out to find the dysentery vine, while the column rested, so that by next morning the children were well enough to go on and we could set off at a leisurely pace. I was in front with Amou, who was making small holes in the sand with the end of his bow as he walked. Suddenly he stopped and pointed at the ground. I saw at once that ahead of us were new prints of large canvas shoes with rubber soles. Amou whistled and the column closed up, the men getting down on their knees and examining the prints carefully. The women frowned: they have no liking for Brazilians, as a few bad ones have ill-treated Indian women they have found alone.

In a few moments Labba got to his feet.

"Three men," he said, "one very big, very high like *yapung*, other short and heavy, other little, maybe boy. Not know jungle, they cut everything." He pointed to the slashed branches ahead.

The prints aroused suspicion: I could think of no reason for Brazilians following this trail, which was far from the usual prospection areas and known only to Indians, so I suggested that everyone wait while Cuchang scouted ahead. He returned in an hour.

"Brazilians. Sit down. Eat, eat nice things, shining iron *gubis*," he reported. "All got new guns, plenty cartridges in belt."

This sounded stranger still. I gathered that they were eating tinned food, which spoke of either wealth or complete ignorance of the better food at hand in the jungle. They could hardly be Brazilian diamond dealers, or prospectors. The men strung their bows and four of us went up the trail. After a while we struck into the jungle and crept up on either side, so that soon we were standing within a few feet of the "Brazilians," peeping from the cover of the trees. One of them spoke in a drawl, and I knew they were Americans. I signalled to Labba next to me, who whistled and brought the others back down the trail to where the women waited.

I told everyone that I would deal with the strangers and that all should talk and make plenty of noise and walk up the trail, so that the three men should not be surprised, but in spite of my precautions they were standing when we turned the bend, with their guns in their hands. One of them was a tall lanky fellow with a floppy army jungle hat pulled down on his crown, wearing a white singlet, a sloppy jacket, shorts, a belt with three knives, thick wool socks and canvas shoes. The

231

second was the stocky one, blond with a small rubbery nose and a grin; the third a serious, willowy youth.

"Hi," I called, "what's cooking?" They laughed from relief. The Indians behind crowded up to see, but kept their distance. I looked around. The jungle was festooned with strange objects, some bulging, others shining, all marked in bold black letters U.S. ARMY. I noticed that the shoulders of the blond were badly bruised and sore where the straps of a pack had cut and they all looked hot and uncomfortable, with a hollow air of youthful confidence conjured up as if from nowhere.

They quickly recovered themselves.

"Just moosin' around," the blond said. I went forward and shook hands with them. Tins of meat lay around although the jungle was creeping with it. Aluminium glinted.

"You've wandered far," I said, and told them who I was.

They introduced themselves. The short one was Ted; Tom the tall one and Roy, who was bent over a map the size of a bed-sheet, the youth. Parts of the map were marked in bright red: DIAMONDS. It would have taken a fast Indian six weeks to get round most of the marked boundaries; ten years to know the creeks inside.

They were very glad to see me and began at once to tell me of their misfortune. They had come through the Copenang with a guide who had left them, and they had no money to take a plane home. "Someone," said Ted, "told us to go this way. If we walked far enough we ought to come out at the Potaro."

I stood and looked at them, appalled. It would have been too hard to tell them that the Potaro was the other side of the Pakaraimas, that it would take those who knew the trails, without boats, two months to get through and that they themselves would certainly have died on the way.

"Glad we saw you. Hope you can help us out."

I told them that of course I would, that I was a British West Indian, and had been in the hills some time, adding by way of explanation, that I had done a little prospecting.

"Anyway," I said, "you can come up to my place, rest

232

awhile and trek down after a time." I looked again, a trifle dismayed, at their stores and admired the toil they must have gone through to get them as far as they had. There was a radio and batteries, the hammocks were tents with mosquito nets attached, of nylon, the insides lined with pockets for reading matter and with small battery bedside lamps hanging from above.

I told them I must call a council and see if the Indians agreed that they should come up to the village, so we left them sitting opening tins and retired to talk, while I was deciding that I liked the look of them. When I got back, all the villagers were buzzing with talk, Cuchang saying how nice the hammocks looked, Amelia exclaiming at the beautiful, shiny pots, and I knew their one desire was to possess the Americans' stores. When I asked if the strangers could come to rest as they were in trouble, they agreed. Then the girls came forward for a look. I heard wolf whistles, and turned.

"Look," I said, "we all live together in the village. Keep it clean."

"Don't worry," said Tom agreeably, "only making a little pass."

"Well, passes are out," I said, "after all, they could leave you and you would be nowhere."

"Okay," Tom said.

After a little more talk with the men I went back and considered the loading of the bulgy kit-bags.

"Look," I said, "split up these things and I'll get the Indians to carry them. But you'll have to give them something."

"Let them take anything they want," said Ted in a half-surprised tone, as if it was the most natural thing. "Look, how about some fine canned fruit here, for a start."

I explained that the Indians were unlikely to want tinned peaches, and that they found all the fresh fruit they needed, recalling in my mind the cool juicy peaches we had plucked on the way to the sandhills. I suggested any spare ammunition.

"Sure," Tom said. He spilled his bag. Red boxes fell out,

full of new paper cartridges. There were more than six hundred rounds. I selected two hundred rounds and took it back in a bag to be shared out later.

"Look," I said, "Americans give these things for droghing. No Indian take anything free. Pay only." And I doled out half the ammunition to the men. As I was doing this Mamiya was discussing the Americans with the women. Then she asked if the strangers with so many shiny things were the same people who flew in the big planes. I told her they were indeed, and thought at the time of her shrewdness in so quickly connecting the two phenomena of newness: the camp kit and the planes. The villagers had never heard of Americans and regarded all strangers with kit as either prospectors or Brazilians.

"Yes," Mamiya continued, wagging her finger at each of the Americans, "all people manager, manager." She had caught this word no doubt from glimpses of managers of prospecting syndicates, such as José, and regarded everyone with a singlet and cap as such. I turned to her. "Anyway they punish now. Lost their way and need help," I said. I told them a tale of misfortune such as they would understand, and we set off. The three boys walked well and were still full of fight, although cut and bruised in many places.

When we reached the village and saw my house they stood back with their hands on their hips and looked at it in amazement. "Where did you get all this stuff from?" asked Tom. "Say, you must have a big organisation behind you to get you in here like this. This is just the set-up we have been looking for."

"Look," said Ted, "we can back you up to any amount and fix anything for you."

I looked around at my rusty shovels and the sieves, the bags and pots and smiled to myself. The place had a workmanlike air of comfort and efficiency, but I hesitated to compare my resources with theirs. They began to talk of pooling what there was, working together and splitting the profits four ways. But I could not make up my mind in such a hurry, and suggested that we rest and eat before talking it over. They slung their hammocks in the hut, Roy having to put his in the kitchen owing to lack of room. We talked till late and then slept into the next day. During the following days I was able for the first time for months to discover from them the correct date and day, and then they started once more discussing plans. They asked what prospects there were around, what I had struck, and so on. I gave non-committal replies.

Eventually Tom told me that they had to get out in two week's time and return to the United States. They had a backer, it appeared, who was putting up a total of $100,000, but they had been out of touch with him for so long that they wanted to find out their present position with him. They intended, he said, to leave Ted, the jolly one, with me to hold the fort, while they returned home to float a small company. They wanted my help. I said I would do some prospecting with them, but that if they wished to reach Georgetown in two weeks' time we must leave in the morning to find a boat at Potaro, below the Kaieteur Falls. I would guide them there with one Indian, but for a fast trip it would be impossible to take all their kit: they should take some ammunition and I would give them meat and cassava bread. Although the hammocks were light, they took a long time to erect, so I suggested they should take the more practical Indian version. We made many ambitious plans, exchanged promises and hurried off the next day with Amou, making good time to the falls. They had fine maps and compasses, as well as directions to show where diamond country lay. They were efficient, but such paraphernalia is too blunt an instrument to find small stones in the jungle.

They had had a rough time. On the way Tom told me the whole story: how they had set out up Mazaruni River which drains the north-east of the Pakaraimas, one of the best-known of the diamond and gold rivers, where the big companies operate at present. Their object was to reach the high tributaries of the Mazaruni, the sources of the diamonds which, from past ages, have been supplying a flow of wealth to this, and other rivers below. They had set out to do nothing less than wrest the secrets of the Pakaraimas at a stroke. How easy it had looked

235

on the map: just common-sense, determination and modern equipment. But when they reached the edge of the ranges they saw before them great mist-shrouded crags, endless jungle through which they toiled and lost their way. It was impassable. I remarked that perhaps they had gone about it the wrong way. There must be some way, said Tom, of finding the sources of the diamonds, and I replied that they would have to find that out: it required time to develop new senses, a fresh attitude and the sort of patience needed to push through a thorn fence without being scratched.

They had finally been reduced by exhaustion and shortages to throwing themselves on the goodwill of some Brazilians they had met. They had carried the Brazilians' supplies and cooked their food. At times they recalled the comfortable hotels in Georgetown where they had lounged at the start, full of plans and visions of success. But they had kept most of their equipment together and pushed on. Then they had joined a Brazilian diving outfit and been put to work building the rafts, amid the curses and shouts of the Brazilians. They felt the pangs of being without their favourite cigarettes; they could not stomach the strong Brazilian tobacco, nor the diet.

"Nothing but meat and flour, flour and meat," said Tom. "If only they had had some peas, or eggs."

"That's the bush life," I pointed out, but considered they had done well to have stood what they had, to have successfully completed such journeys across the lower ranges and stuck it for three months without an inkling of how to go about jungle life. I was still tempted to join up with them if they came back and said goodbye to them with some regret at the falls. Ted was going as far as Atkinson airfield with the other two, then returning to be picked up and escorted by one of the villagers.

On the return trip I again felt the urge to prospect, stimulated by their eagerness, but as it happened I never heard from any of the boys again, although I learned recently that they went back to the States safely with some Indians arrows and their story. They were immediately backed once more with ample funds and have since returned to British Guiana, asking for me. They have gone up into the jungle, but have not yet, as far as I know, been able to find anything worthwhile.

When I returned to the village I connected up the Phillips set to the batteries, everyone rushing about in excitement. I sent the men to cut poles. The others asked me what the box was going to do and I told them that when night fell they would hear plenty of Brazilians talking right in the hut.

"Oh, you lying," went the chorus.

With a great deal of bustle and curiosity I got the poles up with the aerial and they asked me why I put the "chinak" all over the place. This I told them is the magic to make the "radio" play. They waited complacently. That night was full-house in the hut. I switched on and the Brazilian stations began to come in one after the other on the short-wave band. Their amazement was complete, their mouths literally hanging open, and for two hours there was complete silence as we listened to the news, rumba music, and a church service. When I switched off Mamiya was first at the set, touching it.

"*Waki*," she said slowly—"Good."

The men at once began asking how it worked. I knew it would be useless to explain and said it was magic. They went to their houses, and I could hear them talking till the early hours of the next morning, and at daylight the whole village was waiting at the door once more for a further session. I told them we could only listen at night because the noises would be stronger then. During the day no work was done. All made their own observations, looking at the poles and the wire, touching it, putting their ears to it, some even tasting it. Nothing would come to their minds in any way leading to an explanation: they were completely baffled. For a number of days they persisted in trying to discover something which would hint at the cause of the voices and the music; then they gave it up and sat enjoying it as if they had known radio for years. They began criticising the programmes, caring little for concert or orchestral music, but delighted when the Latin-American melodies came through. They could hear in them the affinity with their own

237

Amerindian music which had merged with the tauter Iberian idiom and the deep African pulse to produce a style at once vibrant, joyful and of the essence of all natural rhythm. They could appreciate in the swish of the chocolo the grating of the razor grass on the savannah; in the guerio the croak of the bullfrog in the swamps; in the claves the cricket's deliberate chirp; in the bongoes the rattle and tap of the woodpecker.

For more than two months the radio was a nightly pastime. The hammocks too were closely examined, at first drawing admiration. But when all the village had lain in them they said they were no good; too slack and bulging, the sides too high, and the enclosing zip nets claustrophobic. However, I found them useful, if only for the complete protection from insects.

Gradually the excitement of the Americans' visit died down and a period of waiting set in. I had posted one of the boys near Orinduik to watch for Ted, but no news came and the weeks dragged by. The village settled down into its routine, but I was now neither of their world nor of the prospector's: suspended between, I walked most days, sat on stumps for hours, played with the children, talked and slept. Some days I was in a state of anguish and indecision, looking for something to do and then putting it off. Then I would summon the effort and patch my hut or scrub the shovels with sand. Sometimes I went out with my gun, but my heart was never in the hunt, and I would return and sit in one of the Indian houses, even lolling in their hammocks and dropping off to sleep during the afternoon siesta. I had been so completely accepted that they came into my hut at any time now, unheralded, and sat there as a change from their own houses; at one time this would have pleased me but now, like everything, it was merely a source of irritation.

My hut became disordered, with dust everywhere, hunks of meat mouldering on the side of the fire, my clothes lying about the floor and my gun rusting gently under the window where the mist drove in; the door was always open, even at night, because I could not be bothered to close it. I felt tired and without zest. Gradually I tried to recover my spirits and take an interest in the village, knowing that if I could re-create the undisturbed Eden before the Americans came I would miss little in life; all that was important was on my doorstep. The waiting was destroying my spirit, until I decided one day, alone in my farm, that I would forget the Americans and strike out once more on my own.

Finally on a fine morning I padded down to my farm, on bare feet as usual, and stayed there until midday. On the return trip, instead of taking the track, I struck through some jungle to a ribbon of old alluvial land running about three miles from the village creek, and parallel to it. I asked myself why I should not try for diamonds near home. We were in the diamond country and there seemed no reason why I should not be fortunate in making a modest find, particularly in the flats where I walked. As I wandered along I looked at the ground now and then until I reached a dip about thirty feet long and fifteen wide with steeply sloping sides beneath a bluff, which looked as if a giant bucket had gouged the earth many years before and had left it to weather, and to catch the drift of leaves and sand. Opposite the bluff the sand lay in a long bank; ten feet below, the bed was filled with a foot-thick layer of leaf-mould and branches. The face of the bluff showed strata of red and white sand, fading into a nondescript grey chalk. It could not have been a less promising area from the prospector's point of view, and most experienced men would have said that probably the chalk went straight down to clay without intervening gravel.

However, I had a hunch and slid into the hollow with a wand of springy yari-yari wood. I felt nothing but stumps and went to the face of the bluff. After digging away the leaves with my hands, I saw water welling up: it was black and I lifted some to smell it, imagining that it might be stagnant. But it smelt quite fresh despite its inkiness, and I noticed a sandy odour. I shook it from my hand and began probing again, feeling a soft resistance like clay. There seemed to be no gravel, and I was puzzled as to how the water could ooze through from higher land and also how it could acquire the blackness. I dug away more leaves and lifted a handful of mould. With my fingers I could feel five or six little pebbles, which I picked out and washed in the water. They were perfect gravel stones, tiny shapes, pink, white and grey—all the more perplexing, since all the gravel I had seen in the area was ironstone and not coloured. I stuck the stick in the mould and walked back to the village thinking of the strange formation.

I had been unable to interest the villagers in further prospecting: so completely had I become absorbed into their lives that my suggestions were greeted with a laugh and an offer of a drink or advice to go and sleep, for I had so long been out of the habit that they believed I had given it up and was only being humorous. As I hurried between the houses to my hut, deep in thought, they called out, asking what I had found, presuming it to be a bird I intended to shoot, but I did not stop to explain and went on. In the hut I put a box under the rafters and reached up for my batel, now rusty. I took the shovel I had been using for the fire and banged it on the hearth, found my prospecting knife and a file, and went straight back to the pit. As I passed through the village again some of the men slipped out of their hammocks to watch me, and Peta asked where I was going. To the flat ground, I told him. To them I was like a hunter who has seen tracks, hurries for his weapons and goes out again, so magnetising others that they will follow him. They thought, perhaps, seeing my prospecting gear, that I had found a fortune. But I knew better than to say anything and did not pause.

On reaching the hollow I slithered down the slushy slopes and cleared a four-foot-square patch with the shovel, after sharpening its edge with my file. I was out of practice with the shovel, but soon had a small well into which the water seeped: I scooped it out with the batel and flung it up the slope, then cut out cakes of the deeper mould and put them in the batel, noticing that although I dug down a fair depth there was no sign of the mould petering out. I washed with the batel for an hour until I had worked through all the mould. As I reached the end of each washing and began to hit the batel I saw many small tins, tiny round carbons, felsite, chips of sapphire and a great deal of mica. These were good indications; but again I sought the explanation of the hollow, for such minerals could only have been spread there on the surface by the medium of heavy gravel and the flow of a powerful stream of water. I considered the whole landscape around me and I began to understand. The flat land, the sandbank in front of the hollow and the broken bluff should have told me before that the creek had once flowed by this way and had retreated perhaps sixty or a hundred years before, having gouged the hollow beneath the bluff where the water had swung in a bend. The stream had gradually moved and the drifting sand had held it away by forming a bank which later became part of a plain.

Again I began bailing with renewed zest and dug hard with the shovel, thrusting it each time to its full extent and flinging away the top-soil until there was a sharp jerk as I hit something. The shovel was bent and I flung it down to continue digging with my hands in the seeping water until in a moment I had pulled out a small round, river-worn stone. I wiped the sweat from my brow with my forearm and knew that here was large gravel. I straightened the shovel and went on digging, clearing the mould down to the level of the stone, finding five or so more. In four square feet there should have been a solid layer of such gravel, but I was satisfied that I was on the right track. I washed the soil around the gravel carefully in the batel and found several small diamonds, all chipped, mostly rejects, which I wrapped in a leaf, thinking that if there were diamonds in this spot they would be bunched together, or else there should be a lead to other ground. I wanted to tackle the whole pit, but I could see that with no outlet for water it would be difficult to dig or to wash the soil without making the place a mud-pie.

As I put on my shirt I heard the villagers coming. Peta, Labba and Amou came in sight, all clean from bathing in the creek three miles away.

"What you find?"

"Gravel."

"No. You no find gravel here."

I showed them the stones.

"Where water comes from?" asked Peta. I explained my theory of the creeks' old course but he was not satisfied.

"Water still come, little, little," he said and stepped into the mud to look at the bluff. He was still thinking of the problem as he climbed out, but he said he would do nothing then as he wanted to eat. They left me, but I knew their interest was aroused once more and so I started to work again, clearing a larger section close to the bluff. I toiled all day in the hot sun without food until evening came and the trees on the bluff sheltered me and a faint breeze cooled the hollow, by which time enough water had seeped into my working for me to wash the soil I had dug up. I washed until there was only half an hour of daylight left. As I came to the end of the last heap of gravel, I found much clay and then a large piece of carbon and another black lump, which I washed in clean water and felt with my fingers. It cleared, showing a diamond of about three carats with a coat of flaky brown substance I could not identify. The stone was a good light green colour and without flaw, but the sides were pitted with small pin-sized holes. Still, as I looked at it in the last rays of the sun, it was big and a good reward for the work I had done, perhaps £70 for twelve hours' labour.

The whole village was aroused when I returned with the stone, and the men came running to turn it over in their hands. Even Mamiya became excited. The stone did not mean wealth so much as variety in the daily round.

"All men work tomorrow, all girl work," said Peta.

Sure enough, at first light the next day the whole village, including the tame hog Mikme had taken under her care, came trooping down the hill with all the old shovels they could find, some of them made of hardwood. The work went ahead quickly and we first cleared the pit of all branches, leaves and stumps until the mould was exposed. It was a twelve-hour day and we worked for eight days to clear it, using three of my buckets and four large *gubis* in a chain formed by the girls to scoop out the seeping water and throw it well beyond the hill.

For four more days we dug out the top soil and then came the problem of how to work the gravel. I decided that the usual Brazilian method of sieving on the spot would be the best, using the water in the pit itself. But it would have been useless to wash in one place and then dig a dry section only to have the water run from one to the other, so we drew a line down the pit and made a dam there, the children finding a game in stamping down the clay and sand. The side nearest the bluff was thus kept dry. Although it was the dry season I sent for my tarpaulin to cover the gravel we dug out, for I was anxious that a chance shower should not wash even one diamond away.

The washing began the next day, the thirteenth since we had started, a day usually regarded by pork-knockers as unlucky. But it was my lucky day as I began work before sunup in the dawn mist, with only Labba and Amou with me to hand up the gravel while we shivered in the cold. I spun until sunrise and found a stone of a carat, another of two carats and several smaller ones, all pea green and perfect, without flaws. I told the two others to cut two long poles to put across the pit so that I could continue sieving all day, resting the sieves on the poles now and then for a spell. After a time I made my calculations and reckoned that with what I already had in the hut there was more than £200 to credit. Altogether I took out forty-four stones from the pit that day and knew that if only I could translate these stones into some simple equipment, a partner perhaps and more stores, I had enough lands already picked out to make a modest fortune. I was glad, too, to think that the Indians could be well rewarded, not only for the work they had done, for me, but for their hospitality, which had gone far beyond a business agreement, and my spirits were recovered.

When Peta came down the next day we talked about where to dig next. He looked at the land and again turned to the water; then pointed to the bluff, on whose crest stood three great mora trees.

"Mora grow big, very big. Cannot grow in sand. Mora roots go down to water deep, deep. Diamonds there in water. Maybe in gravel over water where roots go. Maybe roots in clay."

I realised that I had missed these points. Peta knew that the mora tree, more than most vegetation, seeks water, and the three giants could not have stood and grown in all the storms on that bluff unless their roots had reached a firm foundation, perhaps clay or gravel, beneath the sand. The trees were over sixty feet high and the largest about four feet in diameter. The mora tree has a vigorous root formation and it would have taken an axeman at least two or three weeks to cut out them and the roots below. But we had no need to think in terms of one man and his axe, for there were enough ready hands, although we had only knives to cut with.

Labba came forward and said we would fell them in their way. It could be done in two or three days, he said, and all three trees thrown complete, root and branch, out of their sockets, leaving a clean cavity to work in. He called the men and girls and they formed up in a circle about twelve feet away from each tree, and began scraping away with their knives, cutting all roots they found in a ring around each tree. None of these roots exceeded more than about six inches and the work was soon done. The girls left and the men came up to the base of each trunk, where they dug small warrens, feeling for the main tap roots going into the earth, and then clearing the soil to expose a few inches of each. They took their knives and tapped them with the sharp edge, noticing how the bark split at the knife's touch: where it sprang apart with force they marked the root with a wand. These were the main roots where the tension was now concentrated without the steadying aid of the surface roots they had cut.

This search took us two days and involved no hard work. A man was posted to watch the swaying of the trees and the women to watch for surface roots breaking, and the men began cutting the main roots. They cut them about half through, but when we left in the evening the trees showed no sign of falling. Peta suggested that if a breeze arose in the night it might bring them down: if not, we would cut more. Most of the night we listened hopefully, but the expected crash did not come and next morning we were down there early. The children and Mamiya were warned to keep well out of range and we examined the trees. Labba then suggested that we start the trees swaying and I asked him how this could be done. He pointed to a tall greenheart about fifty feet away with much foliage above; it was a slender tree, but the greenheart is well-known for its hardness and is tough to cut with knives. We took it in turns to chip at the greenheart on both sides, with one cut lower than the other, the final cutting being done by Labba in such a way that the greenheart would fall on the mora standing at the end of the row, after he had judged how the creepers interlocked among them.

When it was going we ran out of range of the sharp hardwood splinters and it fell over gracefully on to the mora. The mora swayed forward, the other moras followed; then they swung back slightly, continuing to move to and fro for five minutes before the first cannon crack and spout of sand told us the main roots were beginning to go. Soon the sand was spouting all around one side of the trees, deafening cracks following each other, and the giants shifted and swayed. For perhaps another five minutes they held, and then Peta warned us to move back. The noise and the sight of them keeling over was spectacular, and we stood for a time in silence as they crashed and the dust settled. After we had made sure the last branches had cracked under their weight, we went to where they had stood and it was as they had said, three rough cones torn out of the earth, the trees gone from top to root.

We jumped into the pits and dug all day. In the evening we found to our astonishment that we were striking not gravel but the massive rotting trunks of bygone mora trees from which the ones we had cut had sprouted. This made me recalculate the time since the creek had flowed this way: it must have been several centuries. For several more days we worked in the pits and found another thirty-four stones. Peta reckoned that the diamonds might continue to run beyond the trees to the creek, but we could not follow them with our tools, as they would have been lying twelve to fourteen feet below—easy enough to reach with more power, the soil being dry and light. I decided that we should leave the site and hope that when the rains came they might shift the soil about and reveal more stones.

In the following weeks I spent much time in my hut, cleaning it and setting my stores in order, often thinking of the young Americans and how the three of us could have cleaned out the pocket in the flats and other likely places I had found. Gradually the sand drifted over the holes I and the villagers had dug and soon it was difficult to trace the digging. I decided to leave it as it was without a claim, which would only have advertised the spot to any other who might come that way.

As the days passed I began to think of my future. I had been with the Indians now for nearly five years with brief breaks when I had gone to the frontier for stores as well as the interlude with the Brazilians. I had a fair sum in money and diamonds accumulated, despite payments to the Indians, although I had hardly worked my finds. I knew of many promising places where an organised party of three or four might do very well, but which were too much for me alone. The Americans had sown the seed in my mind of the idea of a small partnership, and it seemed that the time was ripe to go back nearer the coast where I could organise it. The trip would do me good as well and give me a chance to put my thoughts in order: I needed a release from the drifting life of the village, for although there was a strange perfection in the days when the clouds moved across the sky and the paddles sounded from the creek with children's voices, I knew I needed something else.

I suggested a trip down to the falls where we had gone fishing for the feast, saying that I would go on from there to get better stores and return to be picked up again, and they agreed. There was only one obstacle to my plan—the lone journey I must face on the last lap. I could not be sure in my own mind why I decided this should be made on my own: perhaps it was a kind of test that I imposed on myself. At any rate, I felt driven to try it, but knew I must go into training, so for about six weeks I set off on solitary walks through the jungle and practised going the whole day without food, since I knew that I could not carry in my *warishi* the stores needed for full rations.

Eventually the day arrived when I felt we must go. For some time the village had been on edge, wondering when I would give the signal to march. That evening I gave them a brief plan. I would take Powice and Misterisaac, choosing them for no particular reason, and leave them at the falls. We would be a small party so must go overland, as we could not manage the big canoes. The next day early we set off with the whole village turned out to give us a send-off. I did not realise it would be the last time I would see them all there.

CHAPTER FIFTEEN
The Great Journey

POWICE, Misterisaac and myself were soon in the rhythm of
the march and strode easily through familiar country of tall
trees, green light and mountains, which rose in range after
range for seven days. Each night the fire and the murmur of
talk and the iowa scent conjured up peace and rest; each day
seemed no longer than was necessary and we felt in time with
the life that rustled and moved outward from us, it seemed,
to infinity. At last the indecisions were over, a sense of purpose
had come out of uncertain clouds into our feet and our glances
at the trail ahead, our single mind making light of the *warishis*

248

and flattening the hills. We were in full enjoyment of our fitness and the mere fact of being alive.

Then we crossed the last creek known to the village and passed over the last hill into vastness and the unknown beyond it. Mute and passive, it seemed to give no challenge, welcome or sign, and a chill passed through us as we crossed an invisible line and knew, without looking or listening or smelling, that no man had been there before, for we were taking a direct, overland route to the great falls, which no Indians would take normally. In a larger party it would have been simpler to manage the big canoes down river, but we were not strong enough. The trees rose to lose themselves in the ragged roof above and the dimness pressed down and in from all sides, so that we only knew the sky was above because we stood on the ground. Between the black boles of the trees sagged gigantic webs, glistening in some hellish dew, from which gazed red spiders. No bird had dared to fly through these glades and break the webs, some of which were eight feet high and six wide, cradling in their upper strands the leaves that came silently in slow dancing glides from above. The jungle was like a dried, undersea landscape, full of deadness; dusty enough, it seemed, to dry up the sap of the giants thrusting to support the roof of it. The spiders as big as a man's hairy hand clutched their webs and shook them before straggling wildly across the strands to give a fibrous twitch of life to the gloom. Through the webs we pressed and were caught by their gummy clutch; rubbed our arms, made balls of the gum and flicked them off, as we looked about, seized with fear. Even the trees looked unclean: cloudy grey moss furred the trunks and hung bedraggled from the branches like ancient defeated banners, bound in parts by rust-coloured creepers. The earth was encrusted with crackling, rotted sticks and leaves as large as drain covers. Through this giant dowdiness we crept in desperate urgency, following any creeks or small valleys we found, where the blackness was least. Along some creeks, whose putrescent waters lay still and black, we sometimes walked a mile before finding a place shallow enough to cross, where the red bobbing heads of the hymarali snakes would be easy to spot—they would strike from the water although they do not live there. We ate quickly when we were hungry, never squatting as Indians like to do, Misterisaac choosing the place carefully and sweeping away the vegetation where he put the *warishis* in an ineffectual circle to surround us. Sometimes we drove the fear from us by climbing through the coarse moss and up the creepers to perch on a branch and eat as we stared about us.

Above the ground we felt safe, but each time we descended the jungle seemed to change, flapping towards us with invisible wings and breathing opaqueness so that we could see and hear nothing. As we stole along there was a sudden tearing crash which might have been ten feet or three hundred feet away, as a dried, worm-eaten tree fell. The jungle flurried into bat-like life, something wafting through the inert air and followed by a patter as of a giant louse. We knew without hearing distinctly that movement scurried around us and eddied outwards; then even the sharpest-eyed brave with the supplest new bow would not be certain of shooting in time. I wiped my sweating hands and held my gun tighter.

As we crossed another creek on a fallen log which bobbed up and down in the water's flow and sank below as we walked over it, we saw in a gap between two massive crabwood trees a mossy shape about two feet high of darker tone than the background. My glance flickered from one side to the other without resting and I started as Misterisaac's hand gripped my arm. He hissed and nodded at the hump ten feet away, which I now saw to be a coiled kamodie, the water-dwelling python which kills by crushing. Misterisaac and Powice were side-stepping away with their eyes on it, knowing as I did that the kamodie had chosen the shadow between the trees from where to attack, when it would anchor its tail on one of the trees. The others stopped moving and we stood in a rigor from having nearly walked into it, hearing in the silence a faint, slow rasping as the kamodie breathed in tranquil readiness, from which it could leap instantly to lashing assault.

I whispered that I should shoot it, but Misterisaac shook his head. We moved around the kamodie and then he told me that he would remember the place and would lead us clear of it on the return trail. Like most Indians, Misterisaac preferred to leave snakes alone, and had not become so nervous in the circumstances as to forget this. A little further on his voice cracked as he spoke in normal tones for the first time that day.

"Plenty savannah now," he said. "Kamodie wait near savannah always. We try to find big river now for good trail."

In half an hour the jungle thinned and it was as if one were emerging from a devil's junk shop into lighter air and brightness. Now we walked through razor-grass patches which overtopped us and scored our necks with thread-thin, maddening cuts. We looked back at the vanishing black façade of trees above the acid greenness and, for a moment, I decided that I could not remember having seen anything so bizarre and frightening as the growth we had passed through. The trees were unusually large, even for such giants as the mora and greenheart, and the mass of them were sprouting out of the fallen boles of other jungles which must have stood there in dynastic succession from the beginning of time, so that the surface of the earth there is a fibrous mass which could become coal, if it were chemically suitable vegetation, in the centuries ahead. As I thought about this possibility, I realised that many of the trees I had seen were strange both to me and the Indians, although perhaps well known to botanists.

The jumbled log mat extended beyond the thick jungle, with the razor grass breaking into its frayed edges wherever there were clearings. Where the logs beneath no longer corrugated the trail there were thigh-thick carpets of leaves and again the shimmy of giant webs. In the patches of jungle we were slowed down by hook vines, that look smooth but if brushed the wrong way reveal myriads of minute scales similar to those of a fish which rip cloth or abrase flesh. If caught, we stopped in our stride and carefully drew back, feeling the

251

vine's lingering hold like a vacuum being released. But these vines we were accustomed to, and usually avoided with the ease of familiarity.

As Powice and Misterisaac pushed through the razor grass they cursed softly, "*Akay, akay*—it hurts," and soon necks and chests were streaked thinly with blood, and shoulders were puffed and red with the rubbing of the *warishi* bands from the constant shifting of the loads. They loosed the shoulder straps and took the whole weight on the headbands, their heads bobbing along with their eyes on the ground—involving a risk never taken except on known trails or flat country. I followed their example and was grateful for the relief.

We were soon in the midst of the savannah, although unable to see beyond the passage we forced through the enveloping razor grass. I could see the others ahead by the shaking of the grass, but otherwise I was barred in, with no horizon nor landmarks to guide us, and only the sky visible. We knew the savannah must end somewhere and struck ahead. Misterisaac sometimes took detours to avoid swamps, stopping now and then to look closely at the ground or a wind-blown leaf, choosing animal tracks here and there for the trail. None of us felt the risk of moving round in circles or of failing to keep a generally direct path, for it was second nature to move straight across the plain and to remember half-consciously the length and direction of each leg taken off the true course. By evening the savannah was beginning to thin out around ankle-deep lakes of clear rain-water whose beds supported our weight if we kept walking: if we stood for any length of time we began sinking up to our knees. We asked ourselves how we could sleep that night and decided to walk at our fastest pace. In a few minutes I caught sight of a large plateau, or reef as it is called, rising out of the savannah like an island, the first sign being a clump of tall trees which I knew must rise from rocky ground, as the savannah would not have supported them. We passed through outlying clumps of eetae and cukerit palms and walked for another two miles before we reached the reef, where we spread out to find a way up its massive boulder walls. But around the reef lay a black moat of stagnant water and the rocks were laced with camwari thorns, the most dangerous thorns in the jungle, whose branches thrust out from parent trees beyond the crest. The shining black blades were almost a foot long in places, the upper two inches being transparent and as supple as a fine steel needle, ready to slip around bones and through muscles at a touch. We broke down branches from the eetae palms and made a road across the moat, hoping to bear down the thorns, which can be walked on if the foot is slid along them where they lie away at an angle.

It was soon apparent that the thorns in our path could not all be beaten down and we withdrew, stinking and soaked from the foul water. Powice and Misterisaac stood in glum silence, sickened by the harshness of the country. Then Powice suggested that we walk around the reef to find a place to sleep. "Sali, sali," she said. The deer of the savannahs had probably made their hides nearby, and so we strung out and went for a quarter of a mile round the reef, coming to many hides where the land was waterlogged but the beaten grass formed a dry, springy mat above it. We sniffed and smelt the horsey, woolly odour of the deer with pleasure and looked at the shapes they had left in the grass, knowing that they would only hide where there was no danger from snakes or cats. The deer had gone on their usual evening trip for food, but for us a meal was not so easy, as we could not make a fire. Above water the grass was dry and would have flared for miles at a spark. We stacked the warishis, lay the hammocks over them like pillows and sat dozing there all night, shivering in the cold breeze which blew up through the grass. At dawn we sipped the remains of the cassili and huddled our warishis close to each other for company. I doubted then if a solitary man could survive in that country and understood why Indians always go any distance at least in pairs.

As we lay there, our thoughts centered on the little spot we had chosen, Misterisaac saying it would be good when "waiee abu—when the sun comes." Indians always feel that a new sun brings a new day and changes everything. Indeed when the first rays shot through the grass we felt that it was for us, calling for a fresh start, and wasting no time we went straight back to the reef, led by Misterisaac. He was now determined to climb into the trees, and under his direction we cut long eetae palms which he banked up against the rocks over the thorns, many of which, however, slid through the outer flesh of the palms. But the route was safe enough to follow, and Misterisaac slipped off his *warishi*, took a short stick, and clambered up the palms, old and thin-looking from behind, but with his feet coming down with sureness at each slow step, while he flicked the head from any thorn he saw with his stick. When he reached the crest of the rocks he looked into the reef and told us that it was marshy in parts and with many rotting logs with tracks of rats and down from the deer. He moved into the trees, saying that he would climb one and view the savannah.

We waited for ten minutes without seeing him, hearing now and then the tap of his knife. Then we saw him move out on a limb, where he squatted.

"*Brije. Moujee*—nothing, far." He could see no line for a trail for miles. He sat for a while longer without saying more and came down to us. I knew he would like to hold us in suspense and treasure his knowledge.

"Which way?" I asked him.

He rubbed his hand on his *saloe*. "Me no know. Me no know. Sometime." He smiled a little.

"You start, we follow," I said. He turned and took us to the other end of the reef, then struck off at an angle on a straight line without explaining anything. For five hours we pushed on through the razor grass until small trees began in ones and twos and the pools became deeper. Suddenly a hill rose in a slant before us like a disturbed strata, and we climbed through stunted trees and thick brambles to its crest, from where we looked down on jungle. It was as thick as any we had been through, with the added hazard of two-foot-high undergrowth with bright green leaves, a better concealment of dangers than ferns, however high. Out came our prospecting

254

knives and we began slashing a path through it, Powice, being the shortest, going in front, humping her back and cutting a way, walking through wherever she thought it safe. We came to the bank of a creek, which, like many creeks, probably petered out in swamps, I thought, although there was a slight flow in the water. Misterisaac looked at it and around him at the trees and then pointed, saying the creek came out in a river in that direction. No doubt he was guessing, and we hugged every turn and twist of the creek as no Indian would do in other circumstances, lest we lose it, and it led us to the river, by which time it had shrunk in width from about ten feet to a slot of two feet in the leaves of the river bank, and would have deceived anyone into thinking it was merely a little erosion. Most of its water had flowed away in pools and marshes.

That night we had time to build a thatched shelter and made a fire, so welcome that we could not bear to leave it to look for wood and reached back without turning from the blaze for whatever came to hand. We heated the meat, now dry and hard, and I pulled out my old blackened billy-can to make a drink. So we sat and listened to the river. We were sure it was the Potaro, down which we intended to go to the falls, where we had fished before the feast, but this time by raft. Next day Misterisaac and I cut the big corkwood logs with our knives and Powice collected the vines to bind them. Indians seldom make rafts, but Misterisaac was in no doubt about the best design. First we made a base of logs laid closely side by side and tightly bound, and then another layer above at right angles to the first; after binding the layers together we propped one end up and put four extra large corkwood logs under the base. By placing the wood with the greatest flotation well below the water line, we gave the strongest lift to the raft. We built a skid down to the bank and levered the raft, about eight feet square, down to the river, holding it back with chinaks. There was no need to test it, and after the *warishis* were flung aboard we set off, Misterisaac dragging one of the poles with him to pole the raft along about twenty feet from the bank, out of the fast-flowing centre.

We soon began to recognise many creeks and landmarks. Indians see every rise and fall of a river bank, the clumps of bushes and individual trees as things easily remembered. On the Potaro particularly there were clusters of waiti trees hanging over the water every few miles, which were favourite stopping places, and like the fishing parties before us, we followed the custom of stopping to pluck their sweet fruit while reckoning how many more bends there were to the fall. As we let go our hold on the vines and drifted away, Misterisaac and Powice looked back, pointing out with regret fruit they had missed.

We settled down with the mesmeric drift of the raft and talked. Misterisaac asked how long I would be away when I left them and when they should expect my return to the meeting place above the falls. I told him I should be away until the new moon, about a month afterwards, a time which to an Indian is nothing. It seemed to be a matter of routine and we drifted on contentedly all day. Then about two in the afternoon the wind blew up-river and we could hear the roar of the Kaeiteur falls, although we were still two hours away in a swift current—in a boat we should have been only one hour away. Misterisaac decided to stop the raft at the third bend instead of the second before the falls as customary.

As we got nearer the falls we came to a great bend in whose bight the whirlpools and backwash began. Misterisaac poled the raft away from the bank before reaching it and pulled with the pole in a sculling motion to put the raft in a spin. We helped by paddling with our hands, and the raft drew away, crossed the centre and reached the opposite bank, where as soon as we bumped the shore he pushed off and started spinning it in the opposite direction so that we went back to the other side again, missing the broken water. The river was coursing along at a great rate with humps and whorls in the middle. We clutched the vines on the other side and there was a sudden jerk as two of the main floats under the raft broke loose and swiftly bobbed away. We pulled the *warishis* up from the submerged end of the raft while Misterisaac stuck the pole

256

in the mud for them to be hooked on to, and we then clambered up, hauling the *warishis* behind us as the raft drifted away.

After a walk through the jungle we came out of it on to the top of the plateau over whose lip drop the falls. The close, familiar secretiveness of trees suddenly fell behind us and we smelt the sun-beaten gravel on the plain which stretched to the horizon on one side. The breeze and the space were momentarily invigorating and Powice, like all Indians when they arrive there, began to exclaim *"Tukeit, tukeit,"* and Misterisaac became excited, laughing and capering about. Indians like going to the plateau, but they would not choose to live on such a bare place. We stood for some time while they said every now and then, *"Waki*—good." But then we felt reluctant to leave the jungle: if there had been a clump of trees some distance from our path across the plain we should have gone out of our way to pass through it.

We set off over the gravel, which shone in the sun like glass, past piles of water-worn boulders to the head of the falls. There was a ledge where the fall itself was flung into spray, on the edge, that was a favourite Patamona bathing place, and Powice and Misterisaac went there while I walked on down the trail to where there was a cave in which to shelter from the sun. I slipped off my *warishi*, sat down on a rock and felt suddenly disturbed by the smell of decayed tinned food and condensed milk coming from the cave.

I looked about and saw empty sardine tins and pieces of paper. Tourists had been there. The half-forgotten memories of civilised odours surged up, of petrol, machine-made cigarettes, women's scent and soap. I raked under a stone and a cigarette butt fell out. There was a bit of shiny picnic paper, neat and sterilised. My mind sprang to the outer world and I imagined I could hear the voices of people making banal requests for bus tickets, saying goodbye after a party, the listless chatter on a beach. I lit a cigarette, then another, as I sat thinking. Above the roar of the falls I heard a brief shout from Powice; I could see their bodies flash in the spray, framed in the mouth

257

of the cave, out in the sun and the space by the curve of the fall. For a second they seemed unreal, like a sequence out of a travel film.

My eyes fell back to the cave. When they were used to the gloom I saw names chipped on the rocks: Smith, New York; Bland, Quebec; Burnett, Sao Paulo. I began to tremble uncontrollably and was almost overcome by homesickness and the desire to be in a noisy street full of busy people, to see shops and lights. I wanted to shout and call the tourists. I wondered if they were below the falls, still within reach, without considering the signs they had left to see how long they had been gone. Finally, I lit another cigarette, pulled off my shirt and walked up to the falls. I knew a battle was being waged within me that was to be decisive.

When I came up to them I was drawn again to the life I had known now for five years, since I had turned eighteen, and I felt once more that I was spiritually where I stood, by the falls with friends. But again the whispers began and the images crowded in. I went to the water but suddenly felt chilled by it and could not bathe. I began to think as I might have done in previous years: perhaps I ought to get my shirt and put it beside me in case I caught cold.

"Come, let's eat," I said.

They came down to the cave and we drank *cassili*. They jumped up on the rocks and Powice began scraping herself dry with her knife. I looked at Misterisaac, almost hoping he would start a quarrel, but I knew it could not happen: they would do nothing to help me to decide.

"One moon you come?" asked Misterisaac.

"Yes," I said.

"We leave *gubi* here. Come same place. All Indian come."

"Yes," I said. "All Indian come." I was really talking to myself.

"*Yapung*, you go down mountain. We go back, sleep waterside," said Powice. It was still early and there was time for me to make the trip down.

"You sleep below. Soon, when sun awakes you start," she said.

"Sometime woodskin lying below," said Misterisaac. They assumed that I was competent to make the journey in their way, which would have been quick and easy.

They came with me after a while to the edge of the mountain. I had my *warishi* at my back. I knew now that I could not make a promise to return after one moon, but I put it to myself that I could come back one day, with things which I could help them with. But to them it was one moon and nothing else. I turned and started slowly down the slope, which was slippery from the mist, looked back and saw Misterisaac standing there with the sun full on his glistening face, shining like steel as he smiled a little. Powice sat with her hair over her face beating a rock with her hand in slow, resigned time. She wanted to say something and I turned back and went up to her and put my hand on her shoulder. She seized my hand and bit the index finger and stood up.

I turned and walked for ten feet or so, conscious that they were looking. I knew that I must say something, even a word about the one moon's wait, but I could not mention it. I turned.

"Soon, me come back. Soon," I said.

"One moon," said Misterisaac and laughed as if it were amusing.

As I hastened down, I began slipping and bruising my shoulder against the mountainside. I stood against a great ledge and looked back once more. Misterisaac shone from head to foot, motionless but alive, a figure amid the boulders and the roar of water. I waved and called for him to go now and he slipped on his *warishi*. Powice did not look, her hair trailing over her face, as she turned her back on me as if not caring about propriety and walked carelessly away behind the old man. For a long time I stood there, imagining Misterisaac still walking. I could see in my mind's eye the whole band of them covering that patch of ground, Mamiya, Amou the hunter, Peta, Labba, Mikme running between them, and the

259

rest. Whatever took me away was stronger than my will, and I began to go down the slope as if driven. The spirits had decided that I go now.

I hurried down the mountain headlong, scaling rocks, taking short cuts, slipping and running until I was panting for breath. I passed a stake in the ground saying "3 Miles" —the government mark—and I held it to regain myself. In the decline ahead the underground waterfall bubbled. I ran down and dropped my *warishi* on the sand. If they come after me now, as they might have done and with every honest intention, then I would have taken them with me on the trail, got stores and come back with them. All evening I sat waiting until it was nearly dark. As night fell I began to miss them and imagined all that the old man and Powice would be doing, lighting the fire and talking, perhaps about which trail they would take, how they would make woodskins and cross the river. I picked up my *warishi* and walked through the dark slowly for the rest of the three miles. I was without a trace of fear, too absorbed in my thoughts.

The smell of the cashew grove, a haunting smell, filled the air and I walked along kicking the sand. Then I suddenly thought of the tourists and began looking about to see if there was a light showing anywhere. Hitching the *warishi* higher, I walked quickly to the little shack we had visited before and looked about, but all I saw were some more old tins and I knew they had left and was disappointed. I wished that Powice and Misterisaac could be sitting there with me that night to talk and laze before the fire. I slung my hammock in the hut but could not sleep and squatted outside, through the worst night I could remember, knowing all the time that they were on the plateau above. Only the quickly descending mist, more pronounced in this lower land, which came at about two in the morning, drove me inside at last. When I awoke I called Misterisaac, before realising where I was.

I went to the river and bathed as usual and, again, as I sat on the bank I saw names cut in the rocks and my mind was made up. I reasoned that no one can keep all the promises he makes; I would keep mine in my own way and come back sometime, but now I was on the way out to home and the cities. The Indians might understand, for time to them is nothing, so long as I came back eventually. I started to look for the woodskin in the gorge but could not find it, so returned and pulled out the little meat I had and hung it on some poles. My cassava bread was rancid. I spread my tarpaulin out to dry and made my own eetae palm shelter, as a matter of habit, by the hut. The river was high and I estimated a journey of five days. River-bank walking would take much longer, as in many stretches the land came sheer down to the water and going inland would not only mean great detours but the danger of becoming lost. I had to go by river, but the question was how.

That evening I cut about two dozen corkwood logs and worked most of the night on the raft by the firelight, but when I eventually slipped it in the river early in the morning and sat in it, it sank so low that it was useless. I was using the right sort of wood, and I thought I had followed Mister-isaac's design, so I could not understand what detail I had missed. There had to be reserve buoyancy, in case part of the bottom was ripped away in one of the many rapids, so I left the raft, thinking that in the daylight I might tie another two or three logs on the base to improve it. I sat down and ate for the first time that day. Next morning before going to the raft I collected about a hundred cashew nuts from the grove and carried them in my *warishi* down to the river, and then cut down fruits of various kinds and squeezed their juices into some small gourds which I had cut from the trees and scraped out. I came back and rested in my hammock, which was slung under the shelter from some yari-yari wands, with the tarpaulin below as a ground sheet, lying across it on my stomach, enjoying the cushioned swinging from the bending yari-yari. The fire crackled outside and my fruit juice gourd was within reach on the tarpaulin. I felt comfortable in Indian style.

Suddenly I thought that if I did not carry the hammock I could be almost as comfortable by slinging the tarpaulin by the eyelets. Then why not a boat from the tarpaulin? It was late that night when I went out and cut many yari-yari rods of good strength and some corkwood; next morning I walked down the river bank about half a mile to examine the narrowest gorge, opposite which rose a high cliff, down the face of which trickled a long waterfall in the shape of wisps of white hair from an old man's chin, so that the Indians called it Old Man's Beard. I realised that whatever craft I made I would have to come to the bend of the gorge on the far side below Old Man's Beard, to shoot safely through into the half-mile wide stretch of water beyond. On the side of the gorge nearest me were the dangers I must avoid, many overfalls and rocks sticking above the surface for a few inches, enough to rip the bottom of any form of boat.

After a good drink of fruit juice back at the camp I stripped to my shorts, slung my gun at my shoulder and returned to the wood I had cut. I stripped the corkwood logs of all their bark and topped them, to the ends of each pair fastening a chinak which I led over a strap at my forehead to drag them to the bank. It took about four hours to build a box with main frames interspersed with yari-yari laths and despite my efforts to keep it light, it was beyond my strength to shift it with bare hands when it was complete. By using levers I gradually jerked it forward on skids, meeting a patch of rocky ground on the way which took hard work to pass over, so that when I had pushed the box to the bank most of the bottom chinaks were broken. I remade the bottom, and sat on a stone estimating how I could put the canvas under the box. Eventually I put up two poles in the river about three feet from the bank on which I hung one end of the tarpaulin, fastening the other to the bank. It took me almost five hours of careful levering to push the box over the rest of the rocks and over the tarpaulin, and it was late at night when I finally pulled the tarpaulin up the sides of the box and fastened it.

That night it began to rain and I went into my shelter to put all my gear together in the *warishi*. If the river rose I knew my journey in the tarpaulin boat would be more dangerous, for I would go so fast round the bends and over the

262

rapids that some mishap was bound to occur. I sat in my hammock, undecided. I could still see a faint gleam from Old Man's Fall, so I knew that I had a guide to the other side of the bend which I must reach on the first leg of the journey. I made up my mind to go at once before the river rose and so I took my *warishi* out into the rain, soon getting soaked as I loaded the boat and pushed off, without having tested it. The boat sank to within six inches of the gunwale and I was away into the blackness, guided by the fall opposite.

I could see very little, but listened to each note of the river's course, recalling each stone and rapid. I put the craft in a spin: she crept sideways over the river and at great speed forward, and soon I had no control over her; about half-way across she ceased carrying over to the other side and went down the centre of the channel at such a speed that I knew that in about eight minutes I would be among the rapids. I shifted my weight about and paddled with my pole, trying to change the course. Then I noticed that I was being carried round and round in the backwash of the curve on the other side. For two hours I paddled against the current and began to come out of it. I could hear the rustle of the jungle and knew I was near the bank over a sandy bottom.

I jumped out and began swimming behind the boat, pushing it towards the bank. At once I realised that I was in water infested with electric eels, so I turned on my back, as Indians would do, and threshed with my legs, drawing my feet well below the surface. The air bubbles taken under and the noise usually frighten the eels away. The boat bumped on the shore and I pushed it off to take it round to a large sandbank nearer the bend, where I pulled it up and went ashore. Some surveyors had recently been there and had left their poles and huts. I found a small crate with nails in good condition, pulled them out with my knife and nailed the bottom edge of the canvas so that if it should become caught on rocks it would not all rip away.

It was cold and about midnight when I started down the river again. I estimated a thirteen-hour journey to the brink of a four-hundred-yard-long fall with a final drop of about fifteen feet, where I must get out and let the boat take its chance until I could pick it up below. During the night I coursed along, often bumping into rocks, but without much incident. My only concern was to keep away from the bank, especially as I approached Waratak, a place where high cliffs became chutes for falling boulders. Some hours later I heard the swish of water and found about two inches of it swirling in the bottom of the boat; nailing the canvas had made leaks. I was unable to reach the bank in that stretch owing to the strong current and had nothing with which to make a bailing tin except the tiny gourds holding the fruit juice. I found my hands and even my mouth were better and spent the hours till daylight bailing with them.

A silver sheen spread across the water in front of me and I heard the call of the Cock-of-the-Rock and the marmoset monkeys in the trees and knew the day would soon dawn. Soon I heard the large bees thrumming in the air and knew the time would be between half-past five and six, at which hour they come out regularly. Within fifteen minutes the dullness had sprung to full daylight. That morning I managed to bring the boat into the bank and got out with my *warishi*. I walked through the jungle over some water-worn stumps, roots and leaves, climbed a great slab of solidified lava, standing like a bare bump amid the foliage, and sat there catching the morning sun and drying out. I thought I would scout around to find some fruit or game, but found the jungle so dense that I could make good only a distance of fifteen yards with difficulty, the only clearings being around pieces of lava which I have never seen except in this area. However, I found some edoes, small heart-shaped leaves, prized by the deer and good eating for man if cooked. The young shoots I cut were tender enough as they were for a cold salad.

I threw a bundle of edoes into the boat, which still leaked slowly, and went down the bank until I found some squash plants, cucumber-shaped with skins which dry hard and tough like a gourd. They had probably grown from one dropped by a pork-knocker at some time. I picked up about six empty skins, first turning them to eject any snakes there might have been, and took them back to the boat to act as bailing implements. It was my third day and shortly before noon. I estimated that I should reach the top of the big falls about five that afternoon and swung out into the stream confidently. Going along I passed through many small rapids, where I ceased paddling, held the sides and tucked myself as low as possible in the craft to minimise the risk of a capsize. After the first whoosh and the odd bump the boat would bob up and down violently in the disturbed water beyond each cataract: when I knew she had safely passed through, I raised my head again and started to navigate.

This went on all day, until about five, when the leaks had increased so much that I was almost fully occupied with bailing. I could hear the roar of the falls and knew there were only about eight slight bends before the last straight run. The water was by now coursing along at about fifteen knots and I struggled to keep the boat near one of the banks. She became caught in a backwash and spun in a circle; I bailed her empty and pushed off from the bank, but she took an odd course across the river, caught by an undertow, and then swung near the bank. I wanted to land there, where the walking would be clearer, and began to work her to the shore. Suddenly the chinak on the bottom caught on a rock and held the boat; water piled up around the stern, some coming aboard and tearing by in the centre of the river. I was about nine hundred yards from the main fall and forty from the shore. The canvas began to leak badly and I got out on to the stone, realising that I could not lift or lever the boat away from the rock owing to its weight and the pressure of the water and that, if I cut the chinak, the whole side of the boat would tear off. I took my gun and strapped it on my back, stuffed some meat and bread into my small bag and left the *warishi* with my hammock and the rest of my gear in the boat. I stuck my extra knife in my belt and strapped the powder flasks on my gun sling.

I abandoned the boat and plunged into the water to reach

the shore, using the frog stroke favoured by the Indians, striking with both feet together and with my hands as in the breast stroke and then diving for a long stretch, coming up and repeating the stroke. The overall speed is not as fast as the crawl, but each individual thrust shoots one forward at a great rate. When I reached the bank I hung on to a root, having travelled sideways down the river more than two hundred yards. After I had pulled myself out I sat and watched the boat break away from the rock and drift to the falls. I threw my gun down and sped down the bank, swinging on trees and jumping gullies to reach the bottom of the fall, hoping to salvage some of my gear. I saw the boat coming over the edge, as I ran; it vanished in the foam and bobbed up below, but the canvas was trailing from one side and the front was breaking up. It began swinging in towards the bank and I ran on, jumped in and swam as strongly as I could. But when I raised my head there was no sign of the raft or my goods: the corkwood had probably floated away and the rest had sunk.

I went for my gun and powder and returned to the lava and gravel bank lower down where I sat all evening, tired and bruised.

Ahead lay twenty miles to the first outpost of civilisation: only a hard day's walk in other countries, but here, through jungle at its worst, without trails, broken by jagged hills, crawling with snakes and the waters rippling with flesh-eating fish. It was Wednesday evening. I knew that every Saturday morning an outboard driven boat came up from Kangerouma for eight miles and collected prospectors for the return journey. It arrived about ten in the morning and left about twelve. I had two and a half days to cover twenty miles, and all I knew of the river was that it would be necessary to cross it twice to avoid swimming many big creeks that broke up the bank first on one side and then on the other. I could not cross the river in still water for fear of the piranha fish. Only the foot of rapids would be safe, or the rapid itself, for the piranha do not swim in rapids but wait in deep water below them for food that

266

may be swept down, much as sharks wait at the mouth of tidal channels.

I set off that evening, tying the tips of my toes with a bandage of thin creeper, as the ground was rough with sharp stones and roots. I carried my gun cocked and in the crook of my arm, with an iowa torch burning in the other hand to light the way. The birds fluttered from the trees as I went slowly along, keeping station from the smell of the river through the trees. The light from the torch leaped in the branches, throwing swift shadows here and there, and I dared not turn back when I walked off course, as many snakes let me pass in their half-sleepy state but would have been waiting to strike at further interruptions. I crossed strange creeks and passed many snakes, which I smelled, particularly the yellow-tail, through the country ahead. Chipping the trees as I went, I eventually came up to a sheer bluff which I estimated must extend for some distance inland and found there was no alternative but to scale it.

The iowa was getting low so I had to find a safe place for the night: a small mora tree standing beside the bluff seemed a likely bed. After cutting all the creepers and dragging them down, I smelt each of them for the slightest hint of a snake lying above, but there was no scent. Climbing the tree I sat in the fork and rested for the remainder of the night, the second without sleep, smoking most of the time; when dawn came I saw that the branches of the tree hung over the bluff, but they looked too slender to bear my weight. I descended and tried a direct assault on the rock, slipping several times, so I climbed the tree again and crept slowly out along the branch until I was four feet from the rock. I jumped and clung on to the vines lacing the rock, tearing off the nail of my little finger.

Sweating and covered in bits of bark, I felt nothing and found a blind strength to climb the next seven feet. On surmounting the summit I fell over to one side, felt a rip in my left arm and clutched at a vine, with sudden nausea: I had rolled with my full weight on my arm along a camwari vine and had more than a dozen thorns sunk in the flesh. In a panic I brushed with my hand, but only succeeded in breaking off the black bases flush with the skin. My arm soon began to throb and the spots where the thorns had entered showed a deep blue. They had gone well home. But my time was limited and there could be no halt. All that day I walked without eating, except small balls of cassava from my pocket: it was quite rotten with fungus. The meat was a mass of worms and I could make no fire to dry it out from the soaking of the previous days, so I threw it away and went on, with my left arm, the pain beating in it, tucked in my shirt and the cocked gun in my right hand, wading over creeks and stumbling on until I reached a cataract where the river was about a hundred yards wide. This was where I must cross again.

I sat on the edge of the water wondering what to do. It was a shallow rapid and I decided the safest course would be across its upper edge where I would avoid a swim for the whole width and the risk of the fish. A climb up some rocks brought me above the water, and with my gun strapped at my back I slipped in. The river was cold and contracted the flesh of my arm so that I could feel each fiery and sickening wound from the thorns, imagining I could feel them move with the muscles. The arm had swollen and I was not able to swim, so keeping afloat I drifted from rock to rock, pushing off and sweeping to the next. It took me about a bend's length of the river to reach the other side. When I pulled myself out leeches were clinging to my calves, ankles, and between my toes: I had no means of removing them unless I chewed tobacco and spat on them, so they stayed.

I felt too weak to carry the least extra weight and flung away my small haversack with everything in it. I now had only my gun, a flask of powder, three shells and two knives at my waist. I slept that night in another tree, having no iowa gum to travel in the dark. I made up the shells with heavy loads at dawn and tried to dig out some thorns but only succeeded in pulling out some superficial fragments. When the sun was up I set off, stopping for a while to cut some young eetae palms

268

and eat the hearts. I found some wild cassava and sweet cassava and dug up the smaller white roots, tasting each one and spitting out those with any trace of acid. The rest I munched and went on. I was still gnawed by hunger and thought of trying to shoot something, but as I could make no fire this seemed pointless. I headed towards the next fall knowing that a mile above it I should come to some alluvial diamond workings where a notable strike had been made and where there might be someone.

Later on I found some balata plums and ate them ravenously, then some peaches and many waiti fruits by the river bank. There was a mora stump rotting by the water and I tore off the bark. Several cicada chrysalids lay there and I might have eaten them as Peta and Misterisaac had done when we had been cut off in the sandhills—but they had had a fire, I reflected, turning the maggots over in my palm. I sat down and looked at them in a befogged state. I must by this time have been a wild sight, torn and, no doubt, with a desperate stare in my red eyes. I could not face the maggots and decided to clean up. Somehow I got most of my clothes off and lay in a creek, washing my wounds and bruises, sitting afterwards on a rock to dry. For the rest of the afternoon and evening I walked ahead as fast as I could, drinking great quantities of water whenever I came across a clear creek. I came to a deep gully and smelt wild hog. Flashes of the hunt struck my mind and I felt better, although to shoot any would be useless without a fire, for the raw flesh is revolting and tough and I was not yet starving to death.

It might also be a big herd and be unsafe to arouse them in my state. But I had to pass through them and began cutting a path through some high grass, hearing the clash of their teeth, which meant they had picked up my scent. I hurried on and saw three of them. I crouched and fired in the air. The whole river bank bounded to life and the hogs drummed about, so I took the opportunity to dash through and up the other side of the ravine with a high Indian yell, firing another two rounds, and ran to the river bank. My arm was swollen like a tyre and I cut a sling from some chinak. I was down to my last three cigarettes, which was as bad. I smoked one by the river and looked at my powder. There was enough for seven rounds and there was another eight miles to go.

It was Thursday evening and I sat till twilight, my arm hurting and my spirits low. I wanted to give in and call the Indians to help me. I sagged on the rock and began to cry, remembering the Indians and realising that at last I knew what real hardship could be. When night fell I hobbled to the river bank, careless of the risks, and flopped on the sand. It seemed that I recollected all that had happened of interest in the last five years, and still letting myself go I sank into a deep sleep on the bank where I lay. The pain had gone and I knew nothing till dawn; I had slept solidly for the first time on the trip, without a fire, in a hazardous place amid a terrible jungle, and nothing had touched me. I got up with a morning breeze, feeling stupid and without a proper sense of my situation. Then the aches began again and I knew the weary day lay ahead. Feeling weak from hunger, I drank for a minute or so and set off, cutting the trail slowly but steadily through thick growth until midday. A darkness spread swiftly over the sky and the wind gusted heavily. A storm was riding up.

Ten minutes later hell broke loose and the jungle cringed before the blast, the trees turning up in the scouring wind to show light green to its depths, the air filled with the spray of the volleying rain. The darkness thickened and spat with lightning. The water began to rise visibly on the ground and I discovered that the cap of my flask had caught on a tree and opened. My powder was soaked and I flung it away in a gesture of defiance, leaving myself with three cartridges. I trudged on, my clothes clinging to me, under the rain's drumbeat. The alluvial workings showed like toothless gums through the sheeting rain, deep pits already flowing over into guttering channels. I dashed and slithered to the broken shelters and rummaged through them like a mad beggar and found only one small parcel of salt.

I got in one of the huts and rubbed it on my arm. It

burned, but I imagined that it helped. Without waiting I pushed on in the rain, cutting slowly with my one good hand, the rain lessening in fury but still heavy. Soon I heard the Amatuk fall roaring ahead where the boat was due the next day. But when I descended the slope the jungle was a great lake, the river spreading through the trees, some of which were submerged to their foliage. Behind me also the floods had risen. There was no trail and water up to ten feet deep. I stood on a hill and peered ahead, the wind veering and gusting. It blew back on me and, for a moment, smoke wisped up from the trees about a mile away. I knew it was a pork-knocker's camp, probably of those awaiting the boat and burning a farm patch.

I fired a round and listened, then yelled and blew a note through my gun-barrel, but there was no answer. I estimated that to get through to near the smoke would be a two-and-a-half-mile journey and went down the hill with darkness falling, thrashing along in the water as I made my way from one tree to the next, holding the branches for rest every few minutes. Now I had something to fight for and was determined to reach within hailing distance of the others by the morning. I went on until I reached a patch of palms and sank under the surface to the ground. The water was about eight feet deep and I could not stand, so rose to hold a tree again. Ahead I could see the treetops rising blackly and made for the hill on which they stood. A rhythmic swishing started along the water some distance away, I could not tell how far, and stopped. The sound came again. The night was almost pitch dark and now silent.

Every time I heard the noise I swung round, moving as quietly as possible during the intervals. I began to think of what was in the water—kamodie snakes, electric eels, piranhas, and more. I edged away from the noise, losing my sense of direction until I forgot where the edge of the river would be, but remembered that parts of the bank hereabouts were a clear ten-foot drop when the water was low. The noise of the falls was in the background and I had forgotten it in my concentration on the peculiar noise. Then I recalled the river and decided that I had moved far enough. By me I saw some yari-yari wands waving gently in the water with a thick bank of moss and leaves wound along them. I held the yari-yaris and my feet began to draw away slightly beneath me. I realised that I was poised over the brink of the current, on the edge of the river bank. Looking behind me, I could see the water swirling along.

The creature made its noise again as it swam through the water towards me and stopped again about ten feet away. I held on to the wands, motionless, and fixed my eyes on the water ahead until gradually I caught a dim gleam as if a glass bead were being pulled over the water. There was a plop as if something had submerged and I saw small silver bubbles approach. I felt goose-pimples spread out from my stomach. It was a water labaria, quite a large one. I was in no position to face it: even my prospecting knife would be unhandy, and I could not use it without letting go of the wands. So I froze, hardly breathing, submerged to my neck. From about nine at night till daybreak I clung to the yari-yari and then saw the labaria, asleep, coiled on the moss at the other end of the row of wands, eight feet away. I was cramped by this time and I knew that I dare not swim lest the wavelets or the noise disturb him. Slowly I loosened the sling of my gun, held it in my hand and let go. It sank silently. I took a deep breath, gave a last look at the labaria, and submerged.

Swimming under the surface as smoothly as I could I went on until my lungs were bursting and then surfaced gently, grasping a branch. I looked back and saw that no ripples had touched him. I repeated my dive many times, each time groping about in the branches until I found a tree which I could rest by. It took most of the morning until I began to come into my depth near the river bank. Very soon I climbed out of the water on fine graveled ground, where I squatted for a time retching violently and beginning to feel riddled with illness. I staggered on as if drunk, splashing through pools and lurching

272

into trees until I caught sight, on the opposite bank, of a prospector's hut. Three of them stood outside.

I sat down and began to yell. Just then the beat of an engine came upstream. I got to my feet and shouted and waved furiously, but it was obvious that they had not noticed me. The boat came in sight round the bend, a long, red, thirty-foot craft, driven by an outboard motor with about eight people in it. I shambled to the bank and saw a plank stuck out as a jetty. I picked up some large stones and stood on the plank, pelting them into the water, knowing that the splash would easily be seen. After the sixth or so the boat began to turn into the opposite bank, then turned back. The mechanic was waving at me. I waved back and fell into the water.

He raced the boat across and I caught a glimpse of his face, which I recognised from previous prospections, before beginning to lose consciousness. I vaguely knew they were pulling me aboard, asking me what I had been doing and where I was from. I lay in the bilge, propped up, and came round to ask them to get me to a doctor quickly before passing out again. In a few moments they revived me with a stiff rum. They were making for a landing place farther down for a truck to take them to Bartika, a hundred and eight miles away. The nearest doctor was at the goldfields of the Consolidated Gold Company, a direct walk from where we were of thirteen miles. As we talked the mechanic used a pair of tweezers and drew several of the thorns and bandaged my arm in hot surgical grease.

"Look," I said, "if you fellows get to Kangerouma and see any Arawak Indians, send them in to pick me up. I am going to strike through on the thirteen-mile route from here." I knew it sounded foolish but it would be the quickest road to proper medical attention.

They put me ashore after two hours, having given me cigarettes and some food, and I set off along a well-cut trail. When I was within a mile of the goldfields I sat on a tree. I heard some roosters cackling and two Arawaks stepped out of the jungle. They had made fast time straight through from

273

Kangerouma for fifteen miles and found me, although a little late to be of much use. They asked me if I wanted help, treating me as no stranger, so that I knew that somehow they had heard of me before. They put my arms around their shoulders and half-lifted me all the way to the dispensary at the Potaro goldfields, where the dispenser gave me some injections and sent a cable for me to my father saying that I was very ill and asking that he arrange a place for me on the next plane out. In fact I was not so much ill as suffering pain from the thorns, and after a few meals I felt much better. They treated me very well and my spirits were soon improved. The dispenser and another Scotsman, Aitken, a mining engineer, asked me where I had come from. I told them from the mountains near Orinduik, although in fact it was much farther, and that I had travelled alone from the falls, and I told them the number of days I had been on the trail. They did not believe me.

The news got around and the postmaster, who knew me, came to say a plane was coming up and remarked that I had finally made the trip out. The warden of the district arrived soon after and put his jeep at my disposal. They gave me clothes from the company stores and I thanked them all. The jeep took me up to the edge of the airstrip where I got out and told them to leave me alone. I walked up the strip, taking a last look at the jungle. Major Williams, the pilot, ordered the other passengers aboard and I climbed up in the friendly anonymity of air travel, alone with my thoughts. From then on it was a humdrum flight, the others no doubt thinking I was just another prospector, to Atkinson airfield. I walked through the customs. They asked where I was from and I told them I had been picked up at Potaro airstrip. How long had I been in the district? A couple of years, I told them, and said nothing more.

My father was waiting at the gate with his car. He showed no surprise: he had spent most of his youth in the early gold rush of the 'twenties. After a perfunctory greeting we drove off. After a time he said, "So, my son, I expect you to have been to Han Shan on your travels." I knew what he meant. Han Shan was a Chinese poet recluse of more than ten centuries ago, who made famous in his simple verse the treasures to be found living alone on a mountain: the treasures of the mind as well as of the life, and he has come to be known by the name of the Cold Mountain where he stayed. I had been to my own Cold Mountain.

* * *

Some weeks later I had a letter from Bien-Kini, an educated Arawak Indian whom I had made friends with at Potaro on previous trips up-country. He had heard that I had passed through the district and went on to say that "It's been four weeks since you promised to return to the Patamona. I have said nothing. But three of them have come from the falls." He described them and I knew one was Peta. He spoke of an old man who was Misterisaac, and another. They had searched the village near the airfield for me, and would only speak to Bien-Kini. Another letter followed in which he said that he had told them that I had come in very ill and had been taken away in the plane. They sat there and did not believe him and said the whole village had come to the falls where they would wait until I returned. I sent Bien-Kini some money for his trouble and said I wanted to inquire about the villagers. In a few months the last letter arrived.

"I do not know what you have done to these people. What they feel or think, they do not think bad of you. Some of them will. They lost something and I do not think they will find what they are looking for. Two of them are staying here to work. The others have brought their families down and will get work scattered around the mining fields. I know Patamona and they know they are sitting on the route you must come back and I think they are right."

That was all there was at the end. The village, no doubt, is overgrown. The villagers are scattered. There was a spell over us all in those hills and that has gone too. But I believe that if I go back I shall find one or two of them. The rest would follow; although it could never be quite the same.